Cash management

Workbook

second edition

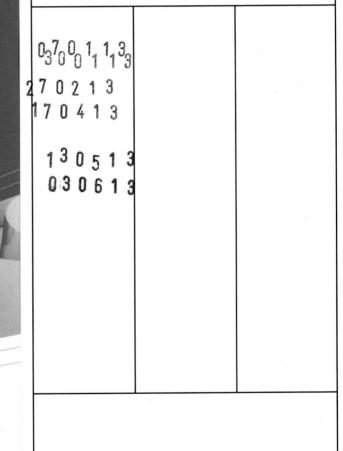

Aubrey Penning

Michael Fardon

osborne
BOOKS

Published by Osborne Books Limited
Unit 1B Everoak Estate
Bromyard Road
Worcester WR2 5HP
Tel 01905 748071
Email books@osbornebooks.co.uk
Website www.osbornebooks.co.uk

Design by Laura Ingham
Cover and page design image © Istockphoto.com/Petrovich9

Printed by CPI Antony Rowe Limited, Chippenham

British Library Cataloguing in Publication Data
A catalogue record for this book is available from the British Library

ISBN 978 1905777 778

Contents

Chapter activities

Chapter activities – answers

Practice assessments

Practice assessments – answers

Acknowledgements

The publisher wishes to thank the following for their help with the reading and production of the book: Maz Loton, Jon Moore and Cathy Turner. Thanks are also due to Jo Osborne for her technical editorial work and to Laura Ingham for her designs for this series.

The publisher is indebted to the Association of Accounting Technicians for its kind permission to reproduce sample practice assessment material.

Authors

Aubrey Penning has many years experience of teaching accountancy on a variety of courses in Worcester and Gwent. He is a Certified Accountant, and before his move into full-time teaching he worked for the health service, a housing association and a chemical supplier. Until recently he was the AAT course coordinator at Worcester College of Technology, specialising in the areas of management accounting and taxation.

Michael Fardon has extensive teaching experience of a wide range of banking, business and accountancy courses at Worcester College of Technology. He now specialises in writing business and financial texts and is General Editor at Osborne Books. He is also an educational consultant and has worked extensively in the areas of vocational business curriculum development.

Introduction

what this book covers

This book has been written specifically to cover the Learning Area 'Cash Management' which combines two QCF Units in the AAT Level 3 Diploma in Accounting:

- Principles of cash management
- Cash management

what this book contains

This book is set out in two sections:

- **Chapter activities** which provide extra practice material in addition to the activities included in the Osborne Books Tutorial text. Answers to the Chapter activities are set out in this book.
- **Practice assessments** are included to prepare the student for the Computer Based Assessments. They are based directly on the structure, style and content of the sample assessment material provided by the AAT at www.aat.org.uk. Suggested answers to the Practice assessments are set out in this book.

online support from Osborne Books

This book is supported by practice material available at www.osbornebooks.co.uk

This material is available to tutors – and to students at their discretion – in two forms:

- A **Tutor Zone** which is available to tutors who have adopted the Osborne Books texts. This area of the website provides extra assessment practice material (plus answers) in addition to the activities included in this Workbook text.

- **Online learning** – online practice questions designed to familiarise students with the style of the AAT Computer Based Assessments.

  Scan the code on the right using your Smartphone to gain access to the online practice questions.

further information

If you want to know more about our products, please visit www.osbornebooks.co.uk, email books@osbornebooks.co.uk or telephone Osborne Books Customer Services on 01905 748071.

Chapter activities

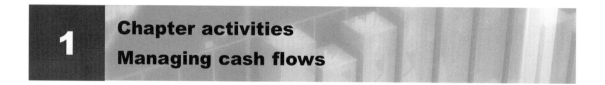

Chapter activities
Managing cash flows

1

1.1

(a) Complete the diagram below of the working capital cycle by placing the options into the correct boxes.

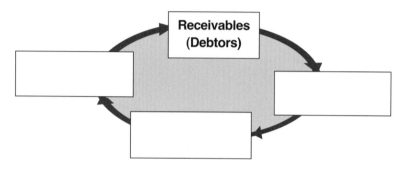

Receivables (Debtors)

Options:

- Payables (creditors)
- Cash
- Inventory (stock)

(b) A business has an average inventory (stock) holding period of 95 days; receives payment from its customers in 55 days and pays its suppliers in 80 days.

What is the cash operating cycle in days for the business? (Select one)

	✓
230 days	
120 days	
40 days	
70 days	

1.2 Complete the following table by selecting one or more appropriate phrases for each box from the options listed.

Term	Meaning	Signs Include
Over trading		
Over capitalization		

Options for **'Meaning'**:

■ Too much working capital

■ Too little working capital

■ The right amount of working capital

Options for **'Signs Include'**:

■ Rapidly increasing sales volumes

■ Reduced value of receivables (debtors)

■ High cash balances

■ Payments made to suppliers before they are due

■ Overdrawn bank balances

■ Payments made late to suppliers

■ Increased profit margins

1.3 Select from the following statements, those that are correct.

✓

	True	False
(a) Receipts that relate to the proceeds from the disposal of non-current (fixed) assets are capital receipts.		
(b) Payments that relate to the acquisition of non-current (fixed) assets are regular revenue payments.		
(c) Payments made to the owners of the business are capital receipts.		
(d) Income received from the operating activities of the business that is expected to occur frequently is a regular revenue receipt.		
(e) Income received from the operating activities of the business that is not expected to occur frequently is a regular revenue receipt.		
(f) Payments arising from the operating activities of the business that are expected to occur frequently are regular revenue payments.		
(g) Payments that relate to the acquisition of non-current (fixed) assets are capital payments..		
(h) The receipt of a bank loan is an example of an exceptional receipt.		

1.4 A business currently has the following features:

■ Sales are increasing, leading to increased receivables (debtors)

■ Inventory (stock) is being increased to satisfy increased demand

■ Payments to suppliers are being delayed due to a shortage of cash

Is the business likely to be experiencing

✓

(a)	Over capitalization	
(b)	Normal trading	
(c)	Over trading	
(d)	Stagnation	

1.5 Complete the following table by ticking the appropriate column to indicate the category of each payment example.

✓

Example	Capital payment	Regular revenue payment	Payment for drawings	Exceptional payment
Dividends				
Acquisition of new business				
Purchase of raw materials				
Purchase of computer				
Payment of Corporation Tax				
Repayment of whole loan				

2   Chapter activities
Preparing cash budgets

2.1   Martha owns a greengrocer's shop and prepares annual income statements and statements of financial position. These are prepared on an accruals basis.

Since the fruit and vegetables that she sells are perishable, no inventory (stock) is held at the year end (when the business is closed over the holiday period). Some sales are made on a cash basis and some on a credit basis. All purchases are made on credit terms.

The income statement for Martha's business for the year ended 31 December 20-5 is as follows:

	£	£
Sales		128,900
Less: Purchases		(50,060)
Gross profit		78,840
Less: Expenses		
Wages	21,400	
Rent of shop	12,000	
Shop expenses	5,350	
Depreciation of shop fittings	500	
Bank charges	350	
		39,600
		39,240

During 20-5, Martha took £20,000 from the business in drawings

Extracts from the statements of financial position at 31 December 20-4 and 31 December 20-5 show the following:

Statement of financial position at	31 Dec 20-4	31 Dec 20-5
	£	£
Trade Receivables (debtors)	1,200	1,840
Trade Payables (creditors)	8,900	7,630
Accruals – shop expenses	190	210
Accruals – bank charges	0	50
Prepayments – rent of shop	1,200	1,500

Calculate the actual business cash receipts and cash payments for the year to 31 December 20-5.

	£
Sales receipts	
Purchases payments	
Wages paid	
Rent paid	
Shop expenses	
Depreciation	
Bank charges	
Drawings	

2.2 The cash budget for Haven Industries for the three months ended June has been partially completed. The following information is to be incorporated and the cash budget completed.

■ A bank loan of £52,800 has been negotiated and this will be paid into the business bank account in April.

■ The principal (capital) element of the bank loan (£52,800) is to be repaid in 48 equal monthly instalments beginning in May.

■ The loan attracts 12% interest per annum calculated on the amount of the loan principal advanced in April. The annual interest charge is to be paid in equal monthly instalments beginning in May.

■ When Haven Industries uses its bank overdraft facility interest is payable monthly and is estimated at 2% of the previous month's overdraft balance. The interest is to be rounded to the nearest £.

■ At 1 April the balance of the bank account was £1,750

Using the additional information above, complete the cash budget for Haven Industries for the three months ending June. Cash inflows should be entered as positive figures and cash outflows as negative figures. Zeroes must be entered where appropriate to achieve full marks.

	April £	May £	June £
RECEIPTS			
Cash sales	8,800	9,180	10,480
Credit sales	53,085	53,520	64,852
Bank loan		0	0
Total receipts			
PAYMENTS			
Purchases	-36,650	-37,005	-42,075
Wages	-18,800	-18,950	-18,450
Expenses	-10,350	-11,260	-13,260
Capital expenditure	0	-59,500	0
Bank loan capital repayment	0		
Bank loan interest	0		
Overdraft interest	0		
Total payments			
Net cash flow			
Opening bank balance			
Closing bank balance			

2.3 Minor Enterprises Limited has been trading for a number of years. The business has requested assistance with calculating sales receipts for entry into a cash budget.

Actual sales values achieved are available for January and February and forecast sales values have been produced for March to June.

Minor Enterprises Limited estimates that cash sales account for 30% of the total sales. The remaining 70% of sales are made on a credit basis.

(a) Complete the table below to show the split of total sales between cash sales and credit sales.

	Actual		**Forecast**			
	January	**February**	**March**	**April**	**May**	**June**
Total sales	18,500	19,600	19,100	22,000	21,600	23,400
Cash sales						
Credit sales						

(b) Minor Enterprises estimates that 60% of credit sales are received in the month after sale with the balance being received two months after sale. For example, 60% of January's credit sales are received in February with the balance being received in March.

Using the table below and your figures from part (a), calculate the timing of sales receipts from credit sales that would be included in a cash budget for Minor Enterprises Limited for the period March to June.

	Credit sales	**Cash received**				
		February	**March**	**April**	**May**	**June**
	£	**£**	**£**	**£**	**£**	**£**
January						
February						
March						
April						
May						
Monthly credit sales receipts						

2.4 Bishopswood Ltd is preparing cash payment figures ready for inclusion in a cash budget. The following information is relevant to the payment patterns for purchases, wages and expenses.

■ Purchases are calculated as 65% of the next month's forecast sales and are paid two months after the date of purchase. For example, purchases in July are based on the estimated sales for August and paid for in September.

	Actual			Forecast		
	July	August	September	October	November	December
	£	£	£	£	£	£
Total sales	71,000	77,800	76,200	80,000	85,000	87,000

■ Wages are paid in the month that they are incurred and expenses are paid in the month after they are incurred. The actual and forecast figures for wages and expenses are:

	Actual			Forecast		
	July	August	September	October	November	December
	£	£	£	£	£	£
Wages	8,500	8,750	9,000	8,800	8,700	8,950
Expenses (excluding depreciation)	7,450	9,010	6,450	7,100	8,050	7,300

■ A new machine is to be purchased in October at a total cost of £40,500. Payment for the machine is to be made in three equal monthly instalments, beginning in October.

■ The machine is to be depreciated monthly on a straight-line basis at 20% per annum.

Prepare an extract of the payments section of the cash budget for Bishopswood Ltd for the three months ended December.

	October	November	December
	£	£	£
PAYMENTS			
Purchases			
Wages			
Expenses			
New machine			
Total payments			

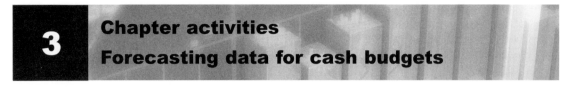

3 **Chapter activities**

Forecasting data for cash budgets

3.1   Freddo Limited is preparing its forecast sales and purchase information for January of next year.

The sales volume trend is to be identified using a 3-point moving average based on the actual monthly sales volumes for the current year.

(a)   Complete the table below to calculate the monthly sales volume trend and identify any monthly variations.

	Sales volume (units)	Trend	Monthly variation (volume less trend)
August	56,160		
September	35,640		
October	31,320		
November	59,400		
December	38,880		

The monthly sales volume trend is [   ] units.

Additional information

- The selling price per unit has been set at £5.

- Monthly purchases are estimated to be 60% of the value of the forecast sales.

- The seasonal variations operate on a 3 month repeating cycle.

(b)   Using the trend and the monthly variations identified in part a. complete the table below to forecast the sales volume, sales value and purchase value for January of the next financial year.

	Forecast trend	Variation	Forecast sales volume	Forecast sales £	Forecast purchases £
January					

3.2 Freddo Limited uses an industry wage rate index to forecast future monthly wage costs. Employees receive a pay increase in April each year, based on the index for the previous month (March). The current monthly wage cost of £18,620 was calculated based on a wage index of 326. The forecast wage rate index for the next four months is:

January	361
February	370
March	379
April	385

If the company uses the forecast wage rate index, what will the wage cost for April be, to the nearest £? (Select one)

	✓
(a) £21,990	
(b) £16,016	
(c) £19,548	
(d) £21,647	

3.3 Deanswood Limited operates a five day week. The data shown in the following table relates to sales in units over a two week period.

(a) Complete the table to show the trend (calculated on a five point moving average) and the daily variations (volume less trend).

Day	Sales units	Trend	Variations
Monday	170		
Tuesday	185		
Wednesday	200		
Thursday	240		
Friday	255		
Monday	195		
Tuesday	210		
Wednesday	225		
Thursday	265		
Friday	280		

(b) Variations operate on a repeating cycle. Forecast the trend, variation and sales in units for Monday of the following week, using the table below.

Day	Forecast Trend	Forecast Variation	Forecast Sales
Monday			

3.4 The cost of an electronic component has been falling by an average of 2% every six months. In January 20-5 the cost of the component is £50. Assuming the cost continues to behave in the same way in future, what is the forecast cost in July 20-6?

✓

(a) £47.00	
(b) £48.00	
(c) £48.02	
(d) £47.06	

3.5 Chocco Limited is forecasting the cost of a certain type of cocoa, which is one of the raw materials for its chocolate products. The cost was £1,890 per tonne in April 20-1. The following index data (actual and forecast) is available:

	Consumer Price Index	Raw Cocoa Price Index
April 20-1 Actual	471	163
April 20-2 Forecast	485	194

Using the most appropriate data, forecast the cost per tonne of cocoa in April 20-2 to the nearest £.

£

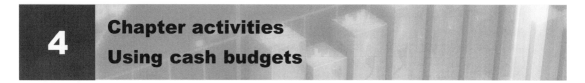

4 Chapter activities
Using cash budgets

4.1 A cash budget has been prepared for Knightswood Ltd for the next five periods.

The budget was prepared based on the following sales volumes and a selling price of £15 per item.

	Period 1	**Period 2**	**Period 3**	**Period 4**	**Period 5**
Sales volume (items)	4,200	4,100	4,400	4,500	4,600

The pattern of cash receipts used in the budget assumes 50% of sales will be received in the month of sale and the remaining 50% in the month following sale.

In the light of current economic trends Knightswood Ltd needs to adjust its cash budget to take account of the following:

- The selling price from period 1 will be reduced by 10% per item.

- The pattern of sales receipts changes to 30% of sales received in the month of sale, 50% in the month following sale and the remaining 20% two months after sale.

(a) Use the table below to calculate the effect of the changes in the forecast amounts and timing of cash receipts for periods 3, 4 and 5:

	Period 1 *(£)*	**Period 2** *(£)*	**Period 3** *(£)*	**Period 4** *(£)*	**Period 5** *(£)*
Original value of forecast sales	63,000	61,500	66,000	67,500	69,000
Original timing of receipts			63,750	66,750	68,250
Revised value of forecast sales					
Revised timing of receipts					

Additional information

The company's suppliers have negotiated reduced payment terms with Knightswood Limited in return for fixing prices in the medium term. The original budget was prepared on the basis of paying suppliers in the month following purchase. The revised payment terms allow for settlement of 20% in the month of purchase with the remaining 80% payment in the month following purchase. These revised terms come into effect for purchases in period 3, and therefore the payments in period 3 will consist of 20% of that month's purchases, plus all the period 2 purchases.

The original budgeted purchase figures were:

	Period 1 (£)	Period 2 (£)	Period 3 (£)	Period 4 (£)	Period 5 (£)
Purchases	30,500	31,200	30,800	32,000	33,000

(b) Use the table below to calculate the effect of the changes in the timing of purchase payments for periods 3, 4 and 5:

	Period 3 (£)	Period 4 (£)	Period 5 (£)
Original timing of payments			
Revised timing of payments			

(c) Using your calculations from parts a. and b., complete the table to show the net effect of the changes to sales receipts and purchase payments for periods 3, 4 and 5.

	Period 3 (£)	Period 4 (£)	Period 5 (£)
Changes in sales receipts			
Changes in purchase payments			
Net change			

4.2 The quarterly budgeted and actual figures for an organisation are provided below:

	Budgeted	Actual
	£	£
Receipts from credit customers	95,340	93,260
Cash sales	20,150	15,400
Payments to credit suppliers	(54,900)	(63,150)
Cash purchases	(4,500)	(3,450)
Capital expenditure	(18,500)	-
Wages and salaries	(18,600)	(18,300)
General expenses	(28,500)	(31,464)
Net cash flow	(9,510)	(7,704)
Opening bank balance	14,200	14,200
Closing bank balance	4,690	6,496

Prepare a reconciliation of budgeted cash flow with actual cash flow for the quarter. Select the appropriate description for each entry, and show + or − signs to denote increased or reduced cash. Ensure that the reconciliation balances.

	£
Budgeted closing bank balance	
Surplus/Shortfall in receipts from credit customers	
Surplus/Shortfall in cash sales	
Increase/Decrease in payments to credit suppliers	
Increase/Decrease in cash purchases	
Increase/Decrease in capital expenditure	
Increase/Decrease in wages and salaries	
Increase/Decrease in general expenses	
Actual closing bank balance	

4.3 Variances between budget and actual cash flows can occur for a number of reasons. There are also a variety of courses of action available to minimise adverse variances or benefit from favourable variances.

Match each cause of a variance listed on the left with a possible course of action on the right.

Labour costs have increased	Improve credit control
Sales volumes have decreased	Ensure available credit is being taken
Payments to suppliers are being made earlier	Increase labour efficiency
Customers are taking more days to settle their debts	Change suppliers
Prices of raw materials have increased	Provide salespeople with incentives

4.4 A company buys and sells products, with a gross profit margin of 40%. The company is considering changes in its policy, so that

■ customers will be required to pay in two months instead of the current three months, and

■ suppliers will be paid in one month instead of the current two months.

Assuming that this policy is operated, and there is no change to the prices or volumes, which of the following statements is correct?

✓

(a) The cash position of the company will deteriorate	
(b) The cash position of the company will improve	
(c) The cash position of the company will not be affected	
(d) It is impossible to determine the effect of these changes on the cash position of the company	

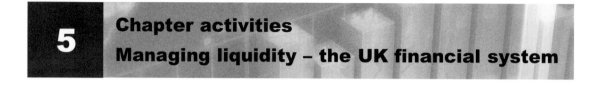

5   Chapter activities
Managing liquidity – the UK financial system

5.1   A symptom of lack of liquidity in a business is:

	✔
the inability of the business to pay its suppliers	
the inability of its customers to settle their accounts	
a major reduction in the overdraft of the company	

Select the correct option

5.2   The functions of the Bank of England include the following:

	✔
it is the Central Bank of the UK	
it is in charge of the financial services industry	
it helps to influence interest rates in the economy	

Select the correct **two** options

5.3   The interbank market is a money market where

	✔
bank customers pay large sums of money to each other using the banking system	
banks make large short-term loans to each other	
money brokers trade bank shares with each other on behalf of clients	

Select the correct option

5.4   Banks must maintain liquidity so that they can

	✔
provide funds for the Bank of England	
maintain an acceptable level of profitability	
repay customer deposits if they are required to do so	

Select the correct option

5.5   The Bank of England helps to control inflation in the economy through the Monetary Control Committee by

	✔
setting short-term interest rates	
setting long-term interest rates	
adjusting the UK Gold Reserves	

Select the correct option

5.6   A rise in interest rates in the UK economy will normally

	✔
increase business activity because more businesses will be able to borrow	
decrease business activity because businesses will be less likely to borrow	
have no effect at all on business activity	

Select the correct option

6 Chapter activities
Managing liquidity – raising finance from the bank

6.1 The main advantage to a customer of a bank overdraft is:

	✔
the customer only borrows what is needed	
the limit will vary on a daily basis	
no security is needed by the bank	

Select the correct option

6.2 A 'variable' interest rate on a bank business loan means that the rate:

	✔
varies according to the amount left outstanding on the loan	
varies according to the length of time left until final repayment	
is based on the bank lending rate, which varies over time	

Select the correct option

6.3 The legal position of a bank that takes a mortgage over a customer's property is that of

	✔
mortgagor	
mortgagee	
guarantor	

Select the correct option

6.4   A fixed and floating charge taken as security is only suitable for a business that is set up as a

	✔
sole trader	
partnership	
limited company	

Select the correct option

6.5   A business borrowing by means of a bank overdraft can calculate the interest payable for cash flow forecast purposes by

	✔
applying the interest rate chargeable by the bank to the projected average overdrawn balance for the period	
applying the interest rate chargeable by the bank to the projected average daily balance for the period	
using the figure for interest paid on the overdraft for the comparable period in the previous financial year	

Select the correct option

6.6   A business borrowing by means of a fixed rate bank loan which is repaid in full at the end of the loan period, will pay, on the basis of the same interest rate

	✔
less interest on the loan than an ordinary monthly instalment repayment loan	
a larger amount of interest on the loan than an ordinary monthly instalment repayment loan	
exactly the same amount of interest as an ordinary monthly instalment repayment loan	

Select the correct option

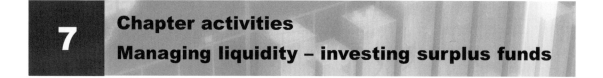

7 Chapter activities
Managing liquidity – investing surplus funds

7.1 A company Treasury Department has the option of investing £500,000 on the money markets. The highest interest rate is likely to be received from an investment that is

	✔
low risk and for a longer period	
higher risk and for a longer period	
low risk and for a shorter period	

Select the correct option

7.2 For the three options given below, the lowest rate of interest given on the London money markets is likely to be given by

	✔
a Treasury Bill	
a Certificate of Deposit	
an interbank deposit	

Select the correct option

7.3 Gilt-edged stock (Gilts) are certificates

	✔
issued by the banks and given a guaranteed repayment amount	
issued by the Government and given a return based on the sterling exchange rate	
issued by the Government and therefore very low risk	

7.4   A business is interested in investing in some Government stock. The details are as follows:

interest rate   7%

redemption date   2016

price   £1.31 per £1 of stock

The current interest yield is:

	✔
5.34%	
1.40%	
1.22%	

Select the correct option

7.5   The running of a company Treasury should be regulated by a set of Policies and Procedures which will ensure that the company's surplus funds are invested in a way which minimises risk.

Indicate with a tick which of the following regulations is likely to be found in the company regulations:

	✔
investment limits for various levels of employees and managers	
the permissible types of investment	
a minimum requirement for very liquid funds, eg 7 days or less	
Bank of England permission to invest in Treasury Bills and Gilts	

Select all the correct options

Answers to chapter activities

1 Chapter activities – answers
Managing cash flows

1.1 (a)

(b) The cash operating cycle is 70 days.

1.2

Term	Meaning	Signs Include
Over trading	Too little working capital	Rapidly increasing sales volumes Overdrawn bank balances Payments made late to suppliers
Over capitalization	Too much working capital	High cash balances Payments made to suppliers before they are due

1.3

		True	False
(a)	Receipts that relate to the proceeds from the disposal of non-current assets are capital receipts.	✓	
(b)	Payments that relate to the acquisition of non-current assets are regular revenue payments.		✓
(c)	Payments made to the owners of the business are capital receipts.		✓
(d)	Income received from the operating activities of the business that is expected to occur frequently is a regular revenue receipt.	✓	
(e)	Income received from the operating activities of the business that is not expected to occur frequently is a regular revenue receipt.		✓
(f)	Payments arising from the operating activities of the business that are expected to occur frequently are regular revenue payments	✓	
(g)	Payments that relate to the acquisition of non-current assets are capital payments.	✓	
(h)	The receipt of a bank loan is an example of an exceptional receipt.	✓	

1.4   The business likely to be experiencing (c) Over trading

1.5

Example	Capital payment	Regular revenue payment	Payment for drawings	Exceptional payment
Dividends			✓	
Acquisition of new business				✓
Purchase of raw materials		✓		
Purchase of computer	✓			
Payment of Corporation Tax		✓		
Repayment of whole loan				✓

Chapter activities – answers
Preparing cash budgets

2.1

	£	Workings (£)
Sales receipts	128,260	128,900 + 1,200 − 1,840
Purchases payments	51,330	50,060 + 8,900 − 7,630
Wages paid	21,400	No adjustments
Rent paid	12,300	12,000 − 1,200 + 1,500
Shop expenses	5,330	5,350 + 190 - 210
Depreciation	0	Non cash item
Bank charges	300	350 - 50
Drawings	20,000	Per narrative

2.2

	April £	May £	June £
RECEIPTS			
Cash sales	8,800	9,180	10,480
Credit sales	53,085	53,520	64,852
Bank loan	52,800	0	0
Total receipts	**114,685**	**62,700**	**75,332**
PAYMENTS			
Purchases	-36,650	-37,005	-42,075
Wages	-18,800	-18,950	-18,450
Expenses	-10,350	-11,260	-13,260
Capital expenditure	0	-59,500	0
Bank loan capital repayment	0	-1,100	-1,100
Bank loan interest	0	-528	-528
Overdraft interest	0	0	-300
Total payments	-65,800	-128,343	-75,713
Net cash flow	48,885	-65,643	-381
Opening bank balance	1,750	50,635	-15,008
Closing bank balance	50,635	-15,008	-15,389

2.3 **(a)**

	Actual		Forecast			
	January	February	March	April	May	June
Total sales	18,500	19,600	19,100	22,000	21,600	23,400
Cash sales	5,550	5,880	5,730	6,600	6,480	7,020
Credit sales	12,950	13,720	13,370	15,400	15,120	16,380

(b)

	Credit sales	Cash received				
		February	March	April	May	June
	£	£	£	£	£	£
January	12,950	7,770	5,180			
February	13,720		8,232	5,488		
March	13,370			8,022	5,348	
April	15,400				9,240	6,160
May	15,120					9,072
Monthly credit sales receipts			13,412	13,510	14,588	15,232

2.4

	October	November	December
	£	£	£
PAYMENTS			
Purchases	49,530	52,000	55,250
Wages	8,800	8,700	8,950
Expenses	6,450	7,100	8,050
New machine	13,500	13,500	13,500
Total payments	78,280	81,300	85,750

3 Chapter activities – answers
Forecasting data for cash budgets

3.1 **(a)**

	Sales volume (units)	Trend	Monthly variation (volume less trend)
August	56,160		
September	35,640	41,040	-5,400
October	31,320	42,120	-10,800
November	59,400	43,200	16,200
December	38,880		

The monthly sales volume trend is 1,080 units.

(b)

	Forecast trend	Variation	Forecast sales volume	Forecast sales £	Forecast purchases £
January	45,360	-10,800	34,560	172,800	103,680

3.2 **(d)** £21,647

3.3   **(a)**

	Sales units	Trend	Variations
Monday	170		
Tuesday	185		
Wednesday	200	210	-10
Thursday	240	215	+25
Friday	255	220	+35
Monday	195	225	-30
Tuesday	210	230	-20
Wednesday	225	235	-10
Thursday	265		
Friday	280		

(b)

Day	Forecast Trend	Forecast Variation	Forecast Sales
Monday	250	-30	220

3.4   (d)   £47.06

3.5   £2,249

4

Chapter activities – answers
Using cash budgets

4.1   **(a)**

	Period 1 *(£)*	Period 2 *(£)*	Period 3 *(£)*	Period 4 *(£)*	Period 5 *(£)*
Original value of forecast sales	63,000	61,500	66,000	67,500	69,000
Original timing of receipts			63,750	66,750	68,250
Revised value of forecast sales	56,700	55,350	59,400	60,750	62,100
Revised timing of receipts			56,835	58,995	60,885

(b)

	Period 3 *(£)*	Period 4 *(£)*	Period 5 *(£)*
Original timing of payments	31,200	30,800	32,000
Revised timing of payments	37,360	31,040	32,200

(c)

	Period 3 *(£)*	Period 4 *(£)*	Period 5 *(£)*
Changes in sales receipts	-6,915	-7,755	-7,365
Changes in purchase payments	-6,160	-240	-200
Net change	-13,075	-7,995	-7,565

4.2

	£
Budgeted closing bank balance	4,690
Shortfall in receipts from credit customers	-2,080
Shortfall in cash sales	-4,750
Increase in payments to credit suppliers	-8,250
Decrease in cash purchases	+1,050
Decrease in capital expenditure	+18,500
Decrease in wages and salaries	+300
Increase in general expenses	-2,964
Actual closing bank balance	6,496

4.3

Labour costs have increased	Increase labour efficiency
Sales volumes have decreased	Provide salespeople with incentives
Payments to suppliers are being made earlier	Ensure available credit is being taken
Customers are taking more days to settle their debts	Improve credit control
Prices of raw materials have increased	Change suppliers

4.4   Assuming that this policy is operated, and there is no change to the prices or volumes, the following statements is correct:

(b)   The cash position of the company will improve

(The increase in cash due to the reduced receivables will be greater that the decrease in cash due to the reduced payables)

5 Chapter activities – answers
Managing liquidity – the UK financial system

5.1   the inability of the business to pay its suppliers

5.2   it is the Central Bank of the UK

it helps to influence interest rates in the economy

5.3   banks make large short-term loans to each other

5.4   repay customer deposits if they are required to do so

5.5   setting short-term interest rates

5.6   decrease business activity because businesses will be less likely to borrow

6

Chapter activities – answers
Managing liquidity – raising finance from the bank

6.1   the customer only borrows what is needed

6.2   is based on the bank lending rate, which varies over time

6.3   mortgagee

6.4   limited company

6.5   applying the interest rate chargeable by the bank to the projected average overdrawn balance for the period

6.6   a larger amount of interest on the loan than an ordinary monthly instalment repayment loan

7

Chapter activities – answers
Managing liquidity – investing surplus funds

7.1   higher risk and for a longer period

7.2   a Treasury Bill

7.3   issued by the Government and therefore very low risk

7.4   5.34%

7.5   investment limits for various levels of employees and managers

the permissible types of investment

a minimum requirement for very liquid funds, eg 7 days or less

Cash management

Practice assessment 1

SECTION 1

Task 1.1

(a) Complete the diagram below of the working capital cycle by placing the options into the correct boxes.

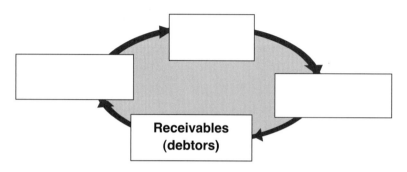

Options:

- Payables (creditors)
- Cash
- Inventory (stock)

(b) A business has an average inventory (stock) holding period of 70 days. It receives payment from its customers in 96 days and pays its suppliers in 45 days.

What is the cash operating cycle in days for the business? (Select one).

	✓
71 days	
121 days	
19 days	
211 days	

(c) Complete the following sentences by selecting the correct options:

Over-capitalisation can occur when a business has **[too much/insufficient]** working capital and over-trading can occur when a business has **[too much/insufficient]** working capital.

Signs of over-capitalisation include **[high/low/normal]** inventory (stock) levels, **[high/low/normal]** cash levels, **[high/low/normal]** receivables (debtors) levels, and suppliers being paid **[early/late/on time]**.

Task 1.2

(a)   Complete the following table by ticking the appropriate column to indicate the category of each payment example.

✓

Example	Capital payment	Regular revenue payment	Payment for drawings	Exceptional payment
Purchase of machinery				
Loan repayments				
Purchase of shares to take over another company				
Final dividends				
Salary payments				
Bank interest payments				

(b)   Posy is a florist, and prepares annual income statements (profit and loss accounts) and statements of financial position (balance sheets). These are prepared on an accruals basis.

Since the flowers that she sells are perishable, no inventory (stock) is held at the year end (when the business is closed over the holiday period). Most sales are made on a cash basis, but some are on a credit basis. All purchases are made on credit terms.

The income statement for Posy's business for the year ended 31 December 20-5 is as follows:

	£	£
Sales		103,900
Less: Purchases		(45,090)
Gross profit		58,810
Less: Expenses		
Wages	26,430	
Rent of shop	9,000	
Shop expenses	5,950	
Depreciation of shop fittings	600	
Bank interest	190	
		42,170
		16,640

During 20-5, Posy took £15,000 from the business in drawings.

Extracts from the statements of financial position at 31 December 20-4 and 31 December 20-5 show the following:

Statement of financial position at	31 Dec 20-4	31 Dec 20-5
	£	£
Trade Receivables (debtors)	680	840
Trade Payables (creditors)	8,450	7,930
Accruals – shop expenses	120	210
Accruals – bank interest	55	0
Prepayments – rent of shop	1,500	1,000

Calculate the actual business cash receipts and cash payments for the year to 31 December 20-5.

	£
Sales receipts	
Purchases payments	
Wages paid	
Rent paid	
Shop expenses	
Depreciation	
Bank interest	
Drawings	

Task 1.3

Chapter Limited is preparing its forecast sales and purchase information for January of next year.

The sales volume trend is to be identified using a 3-point moving average based on the actual monthly sales volumes for the current year.

(a) Complete the table below to calculate the monthly sales volume trend and identify any monthly variations.

	Sales volume (units)	Trend	Monthly variation (volume less trend)
August	40,900		
September	47,300		
October	38,700		
November	41,800		
December	48,200		

The monthly sales volume trend is [   ] units.

Additional information

The selling price per unit has been set at £8.

Monthly purchases are estimated to be 55% of the value of the forecast sales.

The seasonal variations operate on a 3 month repeating cycle

(b) Using the trend and the monthly variations identified in part (a) complete the table below to forecast the sales volume, sales value and purchase value for January of the next financial year.

	Forecast trend	Variation	Forecast sales volume	Forecast sales £	Forecast purchases £
January					

(c) Chapter Limited uses an industry wage rate index to forecast future monthly wage costs. Employees receive a pay increase in January each year, based on the index for that month. The current monthly wage cost of £23,650 was calculated based on a wage index of 637. The forecast wage rate index for the next four months is:

November	642
December	643
January	648
February	647

If the company uses the forecast wage rate index, what will the wage cost for January be, to the nearest £? (Select one) ✓

£24,058	
£23,249	
£23,834	
£23,873	

Task 1.4

Captain Enterprises Limited has been trading for a number of years. The business has requested assistance with calculating sales receipts for entry into a cash budget.

Actual sales values achieved are available for January and February and forecast sales values have been produced for March to June.

Captain Enterprises Limited estimates that cash sales account for 25% of the total sales. The remaining 75% of sales are made on a credit basis.

(a) Complete the table below to show the split of total sales between cash sales and credit sales.

	Actual		**Forecast**			
	January	**February**	**March**	**April**	**May**	**June**
Total sales	48,100	49,600	49,000	52,500	51,600	49,400
Cash sales						
Credit sales						

(b) Captain Enterprises estimates that 40% of credit sales are received in the month after sale with the balance being received two months after sale. For example, 40% of January's credit sales are received in February with the balance being received in March.

Using the table below and your figures from part (a), calculate the timing of sales receipts from credit sales that would be included in a cash budget for Captain Enterprises Limited for the period March to June.

| | Credit sales £ | CASH RECEIVED | | | | |
		February £	March £	April £	May £	June £
January						
February						
March						
April						
May						
Monthly credit sales receipts						

Task 1.5

Queenswood Ltd is preparing cash payment figures ready for inclusion in a cash budget. The following information is relevant to the payment patterns for purchases, wages and expenses.

- Purchases are calculated as 58% of the next month's forecast sales and are paid two months after the date of purchase. For example, purchases in July are based on the estimated sales for August and paid for in September.

	Actual			**Forecast**		
	July	**August**	**September**	**October**	**November**	**December**
	£	£	£	£	£	£
Total sales	79,000	83,800	86,200	90,600	95,000	97,200

- Wages are paid in the month that they are incurred and expenses are paid in the month after they are incurred. The actual and forecast figures for wages and expenses are:

	Actual			**Forecast**		
	July	**August**	**September**	**October**	**November**	**December**
	£	£	£	£	£	£
Wages	12,500	12,600	12,480	12,800	12,960	14,500
Expenses (excluding depreciation)	8,640	8,800	9,050	7,450	10,100	9,300

- A new machine is to be purchased in October at a total cost of £53,500. Payment for the machine is to be made in four equal monthly instalments, beginning in October.

- The machine is to be depreciated monthly on a straight-line basis at 25% per annum.

Prepare an extract of the payments section of the cash budget for Queenswood Ltd for the three months ended December.

	October £	November £	December £
PAYMENTS			
Purchases			
Wages			
Expenses			
New machine			
Total payments			

Task 1.6

The cash budget for Whitesands Industries for the three months ended June has been partially completed. The following information is to be incorporated and the cash budget completed.

■   A bank loan of £75,000 has been negotiated and this will be paid into the business bank account in April.

■   The principal (capital) element of the bank loan (£75,000) is to be repaid in 60 equal monthly instalments beginning in May.

■   The loan attracts 8% interest per annum calculated on the amount of the loan principal advanced in April. The annual interest charge is to be paid in equal monthly installments beginning in May.

■   When Whitesands Industries uses its bank overdraft facility interest is payable monthly and is estimated at 2% of the previous month's overdraft balance. The interest is to be rounded to the nearest £.

■   At 1 April the balance of the bank account was overdrawn £1,350.

Using the additional information above, complete the cash budget for Whitesands Industries for the three months ending June. Cash inflows should be entered as positive figures and cash outflows as negative figures. Zeroes must be entered where appropriate to achieve full marks.

	April	May	June
	£	£	£
RECEIPTS			
Cash sales	18,800	19,180	20,480
Credit sales	43,085	43,520	54,852
Bank loan		0	0
Total receipts			
PAYMENTS			
Purchases	-46,650	-47,005	-42,075
Wages	-18,800	-18,950	-18,450
Expenses	-10,350	-11,260	-13,260
Capital expenditure	0	-79,500	0
Bank loan capital repayment	0		
Bank loan interest	0		
Overdraft interest			
Total payments			
Net cash flow			
Opening bank balance			
Closing bank balance			

SECTION 2

Task 2.1

A cash budget has been prepared for Princewood Ltd for the next five periods.

The budget was prepared based on the following sales volumes and a selling price of £4 per item.

	Period 1	**Period 2**	**Period 3**	**Period 4**	**Period 5**
Sales volume (items)	8,900	9,800	9,500	8,500	9,600

The pattern of cash receipts used in the budget assumed 50% of sales were received in the month of sale and the remaining 50% in the month following sale.

In the light of current economic trends Princewood Ltd needs to adjust its cash budget to take account of the following:

■   The selling price from period 1 will be reduced by 5% per item.

■   The pattern of sales receipts changes to 20% of sales received in the month of sale, 60% in the month following sale and the remaining 20% two months after sale.

(a)   Use the table below to calculate the effect of the changes in the forecast amounts and timing of cash receipts for periods 3, 4 and 5:

	Period 1 *(£)*	**Period 2** *(£)*	**Period 3** *(£)*	**Period 4** *(£)*	**Period 5** *(£)*
Original value of forecast sales	35,600	39,200	38,000	34,000	38,400
Original timing of receipts			38,600	36,000	36,200
Revised value of forecast sales					
Revised timing of receipts					

Additional information

The company's suppliers have negotiated reduced payment terms with Princewood Limited in return for fixing prices in the medium term. The original budget was prepared on the basis of paying suppliers in the month following purchase. The revised payment terms allow for settlement of 30% in the month of purchase with the remaining 70% payment in the month following purchase. These revised terms come into effect for purchases in period 1.

The original budgeted purchase figures were:

	Period 1 (£)	Period 2 (£)	Period 3 (£)	Period 4 (£)	Period 5 (£)
Purchases	21,500	21,200	20,800	22,600	23,000

(b) Use the table below to calculate the effect of the changes in the timing of purchase payments for periods 3, 4 and 5:

	Period 3 (£)	Period 4 (£)	Period 5 (£)
Original timing of payments			
Revised timing of payments			

(c) Using your calculations from parts (a) and (b), complete the table to show the net effect of the changes to sales receipts and purchase payments for periods 3, 4 and 5.

	Period 3 (£)	Period 4 (£)	Period 5 (£)
Changes in sales receipts			
Changes in purchase payments			
Net change			

Task 2.2

The quarterly budgeted and actual figures for an organisation are provided below:

	Budgeted	Actual
	£	£
Receipts from credit customers	88,300	83,440
Cash sales	20,130	25,110
Payments to credit suppliers	(55,410)	(56,150)
Cash purchases	(8,960)	(7,450)
Capital expenditure	-	(23,500)
Wages and salaries	(17,450)	(18,300)
General expenses	(10,900)	(11,464)
Net cash flow	15,710	(8,314)
Opening bank balance	3,200	3,200
Closing bank balance	18,910	(5,114)

(a) Prepare a reconciliation of budgeted cash flow with actual cash flow for the quarter. Select the appropriate description for each entry, and show + or − signs to denote increased or reduced cash. Ensure that the reconciliation balances.

	£
Budgeted closing bank balance	
Surplus/Shortfall in receipts from credit customers	
Surplus/Shortfall in cash sales	
Increase/Decrease in payments to credit suppliers	
Increase/Decrease in cash purchases	
Increase/Decrease in capital expenditure	
Increase/Decrease in wages and salaries	
Increase/Decrease in general expenses	
Actual closing bank balance	

(b) Which one of the following actions, when carried out in isolation, would have avoided the overdrawn bank balance?

	✓
Received money from credit customers in line with the budget	
Generated cash sales in line with the budget	
Made payments to credit suppliers in line with the budget	
Made any payments for capital expenditure in line with the budget	
Made payments for salaries and wages in line with the budget	

(c) Variances between budget and actual cash flows can occur for a number of reasons. There are also a variety of courses of action available to minimise adverse variances or benefit from favourable variances.

Match each cause of a variance listed on the left with a possible course of action on the right.

Labour costs have increased	Improve marketing
Sales volumes have decreased	Improve credit control
Inventory levels have increased	Negotiate improved prices
Customers are taking more days to settle their debts	Reduce use of agency staff
Prices of raw materials have increased	Improve stock control

Task 2.3

(a) A bank overdraft is a common source of finance for businesses. Indicate with a tick the product features which relate to a bank overdraft.

	✔
Interest is calculated on the average annual balance	
It is useful for covering working capital requirements	
The customer can borrow as much as is required at the time	
The account will normally fluctuate from debit (borrowing) to credit (money in the account)	

(b) Indicate with a tick the product features which relate to a bank loan.

	✔
Short-term finance, renegotiated annually	
Often used for non-current (fixed) asset purchases	
Can be repaid in full at the end of the loan period	
Only available at a fixed rate of interest	

(c) Facility letters are important documents which set out the legal relationship between a bank and a customer that borrows money.

Complete the following sentences using the words listed below.

A facility letter is a document drawn up by the...................................and signed by the

...................................in respect of the granting of bank finance. It sets out the ....

of the finance and the ....requirements. A facility letter will normally include a

...................................clause to provide the bank with legal rights and remedies if the customer

fails to repay the borrowing.

customer	**default**	**bank**	**security**	**amount**

Task 2.4

Mastercraft Limited is a small company which manufactures traditional wooden kitchen furniture. There are four directors.

The company is expanding and requires:

- £100,000 for new production machinery

- additional working capital of £25,000.

The company is profitable and is not borrowing at present but finances its requirements from cashflow.

The directors have now decided that they want to raise finance from the bank to provide £100,000 to finance production machinery and a £25,000 overdraft to cover the increased working capital requirement.

The bank discusses the requirements with the directors and offers the directors of Mastercraft Limited two alternative methods of financing:

Option 1

A five year business loan of £100,000 with equal annual repayments, paid at the end of each year. The interest rate is fixed at 6% for the five years and interest is charged annually, calculated on the loan amount outstanding at the time of the repayment.

An arrangement fee of 1.25% is payable at the time the loan is made by the bank to the customer.

The bank is also offering an overdraft facility of £25,000 at an annual rate of 7%. The cash flow forecast estimates that the overdraft for the first year will be at an average level of £15,000. The arrangement fee will be 1.5% of the overdraft limit.

The bank suggests that the directors give their personal guarantees as security, backed by mortgages over their own freehold properties.

Option 2

A 'repayment holiday' business loan of £125,000 to cover both the cost of the expansion and also the working capital requirement. An overdraft will therefore not be required.

The loan will be repaid over six years in five equal annual repayments paid at the end of each year, starting at the end of Year 2.

The interest rate will be bank base rate plus 5%. For the first two years, bank base rate is forecast to average 1% and then rise to an average 2% over the last four years.

An arrangement fee of 2% of the whole loan amount is payable at the time the loan is made by the bank to the customer.

The security requested is a fixed and floating charge over the company assets, including premises, machinery, inventory and receivables.

You are to

(a)   Calculate the cost of the finance (interest and fees) for each option for the first year, setting out your findings in the following table:

	loan interest £	arrangement fees £	overdraft interest £	total cost £
Option 1				
Option 2				

(b)   Indicate which option the directors should choose on the basis of the total first year cost of the finance.

✔

Option 1	
Option 2	

(c)   Indicate which option the directors should choose on the basis of the security requirements of the bank.

✔

Option 1	
Option 2	

(d)   The choice of the 'repayment holiday' loan in Option 2 will affect the cash flow of the company in the first year in various ways. Select all the correct options.

✔

The amount due in interest payments will be higher	
The amount due in interest payments will be lower	
The amount due in capital repayment of the loan will be higher	
The amount due in capital repayment of the loan will be lower	

Task 2.5

Complete the gaps in the text below with the correct word taken from the following:

low-risk   Treasury Bill   Gilts   high-risk   short-term

The .... market provides long term funding for the UK Government. This is a relatively

....................................investment. Another way of providing funding for the UK Government is

investing in the ....market. This is a .... form of investment.

Investment in company shares on the Stock Market can be relatively .... and

should only be seen as a long-term investment.

Task 2.6

Motrix plc is a large company which distributes parts and accessories for the motor trade on a national basis.

The company runs a Treasury as part of its Finance Department. It has a strict investment policy established in a set of Policies and Procedures. These establish the authorities and responsibilities given to its Treasury employees and the types of investment which are permissible.

The investment manual of the Treasury includes the following policy for investing short-term surplus funds:

- The risk level must be low.

- The investment must be convertible to cash within 60 days.

- The maximum amount to be invested in any one type of investment is £200,000.

- The interest rate must be at least 1.5% above bank base rate.

- No deposits should be placed with financial institutions outside the UK.

The Treasury is reviewing its investment options at the beginning of the month and has selected four options for £200,000 which it has immediately available for an investment over one month. Bank base rate is currently 1%.

Option 1 - Blackstone Technology Fund

The financial press is recommending investment in this managed fund which is based largely on international technology companies. The fund is currently yielding 5.6% p.a. and offers a potentially high level of growth over the long term. The publicity material sent out by Blackstone contains the sentence suggesting a high level of risk: 'The value of these investments may fall as well as rise.' There is no upper limit on investment in the fund. Minimum investment is £1,000.

Option 2 – Mercia Bank plc money market account

This is a UK bank money market based low risk product. The minimum investment allowed is £100,000. There is no upper limit on investment. There is a choice of two accounts:

- a 'call account' (money can be withdrawn at any time) – interest at 2.125% p.a.

- a one month fixed deposit – interest 2.5% p.a.

Option 3 – National Bank one year bond

Investment in a reputable UK bank (low risk) projected interest rate is 4% and a minimum investment of £500,000 is required; one year fixed period.

Option 4 – RWF Eurobank currency deposit

RWF Eurobank is offering good rates on Euro deposits, including a six month deposit paying 4% on amounts of €100,000 (approximately £85,000) or more. The risk of this investment is low.

(a) Complete the table below for each of the four options, writing 'yes' if the investment meets County Treasury policy requirements and 'no' if it does not.

	Convertible within 60 days (yes/no)	Available for £200,000 (yes/no)	Interest rate 1% over base (yes/no)	Overseas investment (yes/no)	Level of risk acceptable (yes/no)
Option 1					
Option 2					
Option 3					
Option 4					

(b) State which of the four options should be chosen for the £200,000 available for investment.

	✔
Option 1 - Blackstone Technology Fund	
Option 2 – Mercia Bank plc money market account	
Option 3 – National Bank one year bond	
Option 4 – RWF Eurobank currency deposit	

Cash management

Practice assessment 2

This Assessment is based on a sample assessment provided by the AAT and is reproduced here with their kind permission.

In view of the AAT's intention to introduce International Accounting Standards (IAS) terminology into all its assessments, dual terminology has been introduced by the publisher into this practice assessment. Relevant accounting terminology is quoted in an IAS (UK) format, for example – 'inventory (stock)' and 'payables (creditors)'.

SECTION 1

Task 1.1

(a) Complete the diagram below of the working capital cycle by placing the options into the correct boxes.

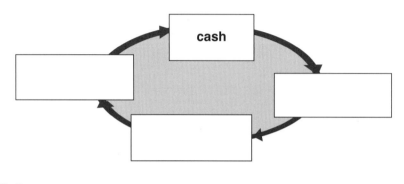

Options:

■ Payables (creditors)

■ Receivables (debtors)

■ Inventory (stock)

(b) A business has an average inventory (stock) holding period of 94 days, receives payment from its customers in 58 days and pays its payables (creditors) in 75 days.

What is the cash operating cycle in days for the business? (Select one).

✓

111 days	
39 days	
77 days	
227 days	

(c) Complete the following sentences by selecting the correct options:

Over-trading can occur when a business has **[too much/insufficient]** working capital and over-capitalisation can occur when a business has **[too much/insufficient]** working capital.

Signs of over-trading include **[slowly decreasing/rapidly decreasing/slowly increasing/rapidly increasing]** sales volumes, **[reducing/increasing]** profit margins, **[shorter/longer]** receivable (debtor) collection periods, **[shorter/longer]** payable (creditor) payment periods.

Task 1.2

(a)   Cash receipts and payments take many different forms but they can be broadly categorised into regular, capital, exceptional and drawings.

Complete the table by selecting the correct description from the list of options below to match the type of cash receipt or cash payment.

Type of receipt or payment	Description
Capital payments	
Regular revenue receipts	
Drawings	
Exceptional payments	

Options:

- Payments that relate to the proceeds from the disposal of non-current (fixed) assets

- Payments that relate to the acquisition of non-current (fixed) assets

- Payments made to the owners of the business

- Payments received from the owners of the business

- Income received from HM Revenue & Customs

- Income received from the operating activities of the business that are expected to occur frequently

- Income received from the operating activities of the business that are not expected to occur frequently

- Payments arising from the operating activities of the business that are expected to occur frequently

- Payments arising from the operating activities of the business that are not expected to occur frequently

- Payments that do not arise from the operating activities of the business but that are expected to occur frequently

- Payments that do not arise from the operating activities of the business and that are not expected to occur frequently

(b) J Wynn owns an office cleaning business and prepares quarterly income statements (profit and loss accounts) and statements of financial position (balance sheets). These are prepared on an accruals basis.

Cleaning materials are purchased when required and therefore very little inventory (stock) is maintained. All sales and purchases are made on credit terms.

The income statement for J Wynn's business for the quarter ended December is as follows:

	£	£
Sales		182,400
Less: Purchases		(27,360)
Gross profit		155,040
Less: Expenses		
Wages	72,900	
Rent of office	12,650	
Office expenses	18,640	
Van expenses	24,118	
Van depreciation	4,190	
		132,498
		22,542

Extracts from the statements of financial position at 1 October and 31 December show the following:

Statement of financial position at:	1 October	31 December
	£	£
Receivables (debtors)	21,620	16,400
Payables (creditors)	760	1,124
Accruals – office expenses	119	241
Prepayments – van expenses	483	567
Prepayments – rent of office	1,200	1,450

Calculate the actual business cash receipts and cash payments for the quarter to 31 December.

	£
Sales receipts	
Purchases payments	
Wages paid	
Rent paid	
Office expenses	
Van expenses	
Van depreciation	

Task 1.3

A company is preparing its forecast sales and purchase information for January of next year.

The sales volume trend is to be identified using a 3-point moving average based on the actual monthly sales volumes for the current year.

(a) Complete the table below to calculate the monthly sales volume trend and identify any monthly variations.

	Sales volume (units)	Trend	Monthly variation (volume less trend)
August	9,360		
September	5,940		
October	5,220		
November	9,900		
December	6,480		

The monthly sales volume trend is [   ] units.

Additional information

The selling price per unit has been set at £8.

The seasonal variations operate on a 3 month repeating cycle.

Monthly purchases are estimated to be 40% of the value of the forecast sales.

(b) Using the trend and the monthly variations identified in part (a), complete the table below to forecast the sales volume, sales value and purchase value for January of the next financial year.

	Forecast trend	Variation	Forecast sales volume	Forecast sales £	Forecast purchases £
January					

Additional information

The company uses an industry wage rate index to forecast future monthly wage costs. Employees receive a pay increase in March each year. The current monthly wage cost of £6,220 was calculated when the wage index was 163. The forecast wage rate index for the next three months is:

January   179

February   186

March   193

(c)   If the company uses the forecast wage rate index, what will the wage cost for March be, to the nearest £? (Select one)   ✓

£7,365	
£5,253	
£6,454	
£5,994	

Task 1.4

Sargent Enterprises has been trading for a number of years. The business has requested assistance with calculating sales receipts for entry into a cash budget.

Actual sales values achieved are available for January and February and forecast sales values have been produced for March to June.

Sargent Enterprises estimates that cash sales account for 12% of the total sales. The remaining 88% of sales are made on a credit basis.

(a) Complete the table below to show the split of total sales between cash sales and credit sales.

	Actual		**Forecast**			
	January	**February**	**March**	**April**	**May**	**June**
Total sales	37,500	42,000	45,000	51,000	58,000	63,750
Cash sales						
Credit sales						

Sargent Enterprises estimates that 60% of credit sales are received in the month after sale with the balance being received two months after sale. For example, 60% of January's credit sales are received in February with the balance being received in March.

(b) Using the table below and your figures from part (a), calculate the timing of sales receipts that would be included in a cash budget for Sargent Enterprises for the period March to June.

	Credit sales £	CASH RECEIVED				
		February £	March £	April £	May £	June £
January						
February						
March						
April						
May						
Monthly credit sales receipts						

Task 1.5

Fortnum Ltd is preparing cash payment figures ready for inclusion in a cash budget. The following information is relevant to the payment patterns for purchases, wages and expenses.

■ Purchases are calculated as 55% of the next month's forecast sales and are paid two months after the date of purchase. For example, purchases in July are based on the estimated sales for August and paid for in September.

	Actual			**Forecast**		
	July	**August**	**September**	**October**	**November**	**December**
	£	£	£	£	£	£
Total sales	84,000	86,700	85,300	89,000	90,600	91,200

■ Wages are paid in the month that they are incurred and expenses are paid in the month after they are incurred. The actual and forecast figures for wages and expenses are:

	Actual			**Forecast**		
	July	**August**	**September**	**October**	**November**	**December**
	£	£	£	£	£	£
Wages	11,750	11,750	12,000	12,300	12,300	12,750
Expenses (excluding depreciation)	5,808	6,879	7,470	8,836	7,652	7,478

■ A new machine is to be purchased in October at a total cost of £45,000. Payment for the machine is to be made in three equal monthly instalments, beginning in October.

■ The machine is to be depreciated monthly on a straight-line basis at 20% per annum.

Prepare an extract of the payments section of the cash budget for Fortnum Ltd for the three months ended December.

	October £	November £	December £
PAYMENTS			
Purchases			
Wages			
Expenses			
New machine			
Total payments			

Task 1.6

The cash budget for Goran Industries for the three months ended June has been partially completed. The following information is to be incorporated and the cash budget completed.

■   A bank loan of £43,200 has been negotiated and this will be paid into the business bank account in April.

■   The principal (capital) element of the bank loan (£43,200) is to be repaid in 48 equal monthly instalments beginning in May.

■   The loan attracts 5% interest per annum calculated on the amount of the loan principal advanced in April. The annual interest charge is to be paid in equal monthly instalments beginning in May.

■   When Goran Industries uses its bank overdraft facility interest is payable monthly and is estimated at 1% of the previous month's overdraft balance. The interest is to be rounded to the nearest £.

■   At 1 April the balance of the bank account was £4,232.

Using the additional information above, complete the cash budget for Goran Industries for the three months ending June. Cash inflows should be entered as positive figures and cash outflows as negative figures. Zeroes must be entered where appropriate to achieve full marks.

	April	May	June
	£	£	£
RECEIPTS			
Cash sales	8,100	9,180	10,440
Credit sales	53,064	53,516	64,152
Bank loan		0	0
Total receipts			
PAYMENTS			
Purchases	-34,650	-37,125	-42,075
Wages	-18,000	-18,450	-18,450
Expenses	-10,318	-11,269	-13,254
Capital expenditure	0	-49,500	0
Bank loan capital repayment	0		
Bank loan interest	0		
Overdraft interest	0		
Total payments			
Net cash flow	41,396		
Opening bank balance			
Closing bank balance			

SECTION 2

Task 2.1

A cash budget has been prepared for Inzyz Ltd for the next five periods.

The budget was prepared based on the following sales volumes and a selling price of £24 per item.

	Period 1	Period 2	Period 3	Period 4	Period 5
Sales volume (items)	1,150	1,200	1,230	1,260	1,300

The pattern of cash receipts used in the budget assumed 50% of sales were received in the month of sale and the remaining 50% in the month following sale.

In the light of current economic trends Inzyz Ltd needs to adjust its cash budget to take account of the following:

■   The selling price from period 1 will be reduced by 15% per item.

■   The pattern of sales receipts changes to 25% of sales received in the month of sale, 50% in the month following sale and the remaining 25% two months after sale.

(a)   Use the table below to calculate the effect of the changes in the forecast amounts and timing of cash receipts for periods 3, 4 and 5:

	Period 1 (£)	Period 2 (£)	Period 3 (£)	Period 4 (£)	Period 5 (£)
Original value of forecast sales	27,600	28,800	29,520	30,240	31,200
Original timing of receipts			29,160	29,880	30,720
Revised value of forecast sales					
Revised timing of receipts					

Additional information

The company has managed to negotiate extended payment terms with its suppliers. The original budget was prepared on the basis of paying suppliers in the month following purchase. The revised payment terms allow for settlement of 30% in the month following purchase with the remaining payment two months after purchase.

The original budgeted purchase figures were:

	Period 1 *(£)*	Period 2 *(£)*	Period 3 *(£)*	Period 4 *(£)*	Period 5 *(£)*
Purchases	8,480	9,600	9,820	10,940	11,110

(b)   Use the table below to calculate the effect of the changes in the timing of purchase payments for periods 3, 4 and 5:

	Period 3 *(£)*	Period 4 *(£)*	Period 5 *(£)*
Original timing of payments			
Revised timing of payments			

(c)   Using your calculations from parts (a) and (b), complete the table to show the net effect of the changes to sales receipts and purchase payments for periods 3, 4 and 5.

	Period 3 *(£)*	Period 4 *(£)*	Period 5 *(£)*
Changes in sales receipts			
Changes in purchase payments			
Net change			

Task 2.2

The quarterly budgeted and actual figures for an organisation are provided below:

	Budgeted	Actual
	£	£
Receipts from receivables (debtors)	86,423	81,667
Cash sales	14,350	11,780
Payments to payables (creditors)	(42,618)	(44,791)
Cash purchases	(7,600)	(7,940)
Capital expenditure	-	(28,000)
Wages and salaries	(19,200)	(17,600)
General expenses	(24,650)	(22,464)
Net cash flow	6,705	(27,348)
Opening bank balance	4,200	4,200
Closing bank balance	10,905	(23,148)

(a) Prepare a reconciliation of budgeted cash flow with actual cash flow for the quarter. Select the appropriate description for each entry.

	£
Budgeted closing bank balance	
Surplus/Shortfall in receipts from receivables (debtors)	
Surplus/Shortfall in cash sales	
Increase/Decrease in payments to payables (creditors)	
Increase/Decrease in cash purchases	
Increase/Decrease in capital expenditure	
Increase/Decrease in wages and salaries	
Increase/Decrease in general expenses	
Actual closing bank balance	

(b)   Which actions (taken in isolation) would have avoided an overdrawn bank balance?

	✓
(a) Chased customers to pay sooner and delayed payments to payables (creditors)	
(b) Increased cash sales through better marketing	
(c) Delayed capital expenditure	
(d) Negotiated lower wages payments to employees	

(c)   Variances between budget and actual cash flows can occur for a number of reasons. There are also a variety of courses of action available to minimise adverse variances or benefit from favourable variances.

Match each cause of a variance listed on the left with a possible course of action on the right.

Labour costs have increased	Improve credit control
Sales volumes have decreased	Change suppliers
Payments to suppliers are being made earlier	Reduce overtime working
Customers are taking more days to settle their debts	Negotiate early settlement discount
Prices of raw materials have increased	Improve the product

Task 2.3

(a) Which of the following best describes the main features of an overdraft? (Tick one)

✓

Interest rates are low; it is available for as long as required; it is useful for capital purchases.	
Interest rates are low; it is payable on demand; it is useful for capital purchases.	
Interest rates are low; repayments can be negotiated; it is useful for capital purchases.	
Interest rates are high; repayments can be negotiated; it is a short-term form of finance.	
Interest rates are high; it is repayable on demand; it is a short-term form of finance.	
Interest rates are high; it is available for as long as required; it is a long-term form of finance.	

(b) Which of the following best describes the main features of a bank loan? (Tick one)

✓

Interest rates are low; it is available for as long as required; it is useful for capital purchases.	
Interest rates are low; it is payable on demand; it is useful for capital purchases.	
Interest rates are low; repayments can be negotiated; it is useful for capital purchases.	
Interest rates are high; repayments can be negotiated; it is a short-term form of finance.	
Interest rates are high; it is repayable on demand; it is a short-term form of finance.	
Interest rates are high; it is available for as long as required; it is a long-term form of finance.	

(c) Complete the sentences below by picking the correct options.

A bank facility letter sets out the **[draft/ possible/ legal/ illegal]** rights and duties of **[the bank/ the customer/ the bank and the customer]** when the bank grants **[an overdraft facility/ a bank loan/ overdrafts and loans]**.

The purpose of a facility letter is to protect the rights of **[the bank/ the customer/ the bank and the customer]**.

Task 2.4

The three partner firm of Parry & Associates is planning to expand its production facilities. The expansion plans will require the purchase of new machinery at a cost of £78,000 and a working capital injection of £18,000.

The partnership has been seeking possible means of funding the expansion and has been offered three options:

Option 1

A bank loan of £78,000 secured on the new machinery. Capital repayments are to be made over four years in equal instalments. The interest rate is fixed at 6% per annum calculated on the capital balance outstanding at the beginning of each year.

An arrangement fee equal to 1% of the bank loan is payable at the beginning of the loan term.

The bank is also offering an overdraft facility of £19,500 which attracts an annual interest rate of 12%. The partners believe that they will require an average overdraft of £16,000 for eight months of the first year.

Option 2

A bank loan of £96,000 secured on the assets of the partnership. Principal (capital) repayments are to be made over four years, with a four month payment holiday at the beginning of the loan term. (This means that repayments of the principal will not begin until the fifth month after the loan is received by the partnership.)

The interest rate is fixed at 6.5% per annum for the first two years and will then revert to a variable interest rate set at 3% above the base rate.

An arrangement fee equal to 0.75% of the bank loan is payable at the beginning of the loan term.

Under this option there will be no requirement for a bank overdraft facility.

Option 3

Each of the three partners will take out a personal secured loan of £32,000 repayable over five years at an interest rate of 2.5%. These monies will then be loaned to the partnership as increased capital. Interest of 4% per annum is payable by the partnership to the partners.

Under this option there will be no requirement for a bank overdraft facility.

An extract from the partnership policy in respect of raising finance states the following:

- The maximum overdraft facility that the partnership may obtain is £20,000.

- Interest payable by the partnership is to be kept as low as possible.

- Loan finance may be secured on the assets of the partnership.

- The partners should not give personal guarantees or security for loan finance.

(a) Complete the table below to calculate the cost to the partnership for the first year of financing under each of the three options:

	Loan interest £	Arrangement fee £	Overdraft interest £	Total cost £
Option 1				
Option 2				
Option 3				

(b) Which financing option should the partnership select taking account of the provision of the partnership policy? (Tick one)

✓

Option 1	
Option 2	
Option 3	
None of the options	

Task 2.5

Select the correct options to complete the following sentences:

Certificates of deposit are certificates issued by **[banks/ companies/ stock exchange/ local authority]** that certify that an amount of money has been deposited and will be repaid at a specific date in the future. They **[can/cannot]** be traded on a market. They are considered to be a **[low risk/high risk]** investment.

Local authority short-term loans are certificates issued by **[banks/ companies/ stock exchange/ local authorities]** and backed by the government. They **[can/cannot]** be traded on a market. They are considered to be a **[low risk bank loan/high risk bank loan/low risk investment/high risk investment]**.

Government securities are also known as **[gold-edged/ gilt-edged/ gilted]** securities and **[can/cannot]** be traded. Interest rates are **[fixed/variable]** and these types of securities are considered to be **[low risk/ high risk]** because **[they are/are not]** backed by the government.

Task 2.6

The investment manual of a treasury department in a large company has the following policy for investing surplus funds:

■   The investment must be convertible to cash within 60 days.

■   The maximum amount to be invested in any one type of investment is £50,000.

■   The interest rate must be at least 2% above base rate which is currently 0.5%.

■   The investment must not include shares.

■   Only low or medium risk investments are to be selected.

Four possible investment options are available:

Option 1

Investment of £50,000 required; 90-day notice period; medium risk; investment portfolio includes shares; interest rate is 2.8% per annum.

Option 2

Maximum investment is £80,000 and minimum investment is £30,000; 30-day notice period; interest rate is 1.5% above base rate; low risk; does not include investment in shares.

Option 3

Investment portfolio comprises stocks and shares; high risk; projected interest rate is 7% and a minimum investment of £40,000 is required; 45-day notice period.

Option 4

Low risk; guaranteed return of 3% per annum; no stocks or shares; minimum investment of £52,000; 7-day notice period.

(a)   Complete the table below to show which of the policy requirements are met by each of the four options. State 'yes' or 'no' in each box.

	Convertible within 60 days	Investment £50,000 or below	Interest rate 2% above base	Investment does not include shares	Risk
Option 1					
Option 2					
Option 3					
Option 4					

(b)   Complete the sentence to recommend which of the options, if any, should be selected.

The company should select **[Option 1/Option 2/Option 3/Option 4/ none of the options]**.

Cash management

Practice assessment 3

SECTION 1

Task 1.1

(a) Select which of the following statement(s) regarding the cash cycle are true, and which are false.

✔

Statement	True	False
(a) If there is no inventory held, and the receivables days are equal to the payables days, the cash cycle will be zero		
(b) If the payables days are greater than the receivables days, the cash cycle will always be negative		
(c) Assuming no change in receivables days or inventory days, the greater the payables days; the longer the cash cycle		
(d) Assuming no change in payables days or inventory days, the greater the receivables days; the longer the cash cycle		

(b) If the inventory holding period reduces by 13 days and the payables days increases by 10 days, what is the impact on the cash operating cycle? (Select one)

✔

(a) increase by 3 days	
(b) increase by 23 days	
(c) reduce by 3 days	
(d) reduce by 23 days	

(c) Identify whether each of the statements is a correct or incorrect indicator of possible over-capitalisation.

✔

	Correct	Incorrect
(a) Increased use of overdraft facility		
(b) High levels of slow moving inventory		
(c) Payments made to suppliers before due		
(d) High levels of receivables with ineffective credit control		
(e) High cash and bank balances		

Task 1.2

(a)   Identify whether each of the following statements is true or false.

✔

	True	False
(a) Profit on the sale of non-current assets is an example of an exceptional receipt		
(b) If a non-current asset with a carrying amount of £5,000 was sold for cash at a profit of £500, the proceeds would be £5,500		
(c) Proceeds on disposal of non-current assets should be incorporated into cash statements regardless of whether they result in profits or losses		
(d) If a non-current asset had an original cost of £12,000 and accumulated depreciation of £4,500 was sold for cash at a loss of £3,200, the proceeds would be £10,700		

(b)   The carrying amount of plant and equipment at 1 July was £290,500, and at 30 September was £315,650. The depreciation charge recorded in the income statement for the period between these dates was £31,450. There were no disposals of plant and equipment during this period.

The additions to plant and equipment were all paid in cash, and this amounted to   £ [   ]

(c)   The balance of trade payables at 1 July was £441,325, and the balance at 30 September was £395,460. Credit purchases in the period between these dates amounted to £294,600, and purchase returns were £15,300.

The total cash paid to credit suppliers between 1 July and 30 September was   £ [   ]

(d)   Identify the most appropriate description for capital payments.

Description	✔
(a) Payments to the owners of the business	
(b) Payments to acquire non-current assets	
(c) Payments that are not expected to occur frequently	
(d) Payments that are expected to occur regularly	

Task 1.3

Jumbo Limited is preparing its forecast sales and purchase information.

The sales value trend is to be identified using a 3-point moving average based on the actual monthly sales values for the current year.

(a) Complete the table below to calculate the monthly sales value trend and identify any monthly variations.

	Sales value £	Trend £
August	163,600	
September	189,200	
October	154,800	
November	167,200	
December	192,800	

The monthly sales value trend is   £

(b) The selling price per unit has been set at £25.

The monthly sales volume trend is   units

(c)   The company has identified the following regular monthly variations:

Month	Variation £
January	- 15,600
February	- 4,400
March	+ 20,000

Complete the following table to forecast sales for the January, February and March immediately following the months in the table in part (a).

	Trend £	Monthly Variation £	Forecast Sales Value £
January			
February			
March			

(d)   The direct labour used in a product currently cost £9.50 per hour. Each unit of the product takes 15 minutes direct labour time to manufacture.

The labour force is to receive a 3% pay increase.

In future, the direct labour cost to manufacture 20,000 units will be   £ _____

Task 1.4

An organisation has analysed its sales and concluded that 25% of sales are made on a cash basis and 75% on a credit basis.

The organisation manufactures a single product with a selling price of £60 per unit.

The forecast sales volumes for September to December are:

September	October	November	December
1,100 units	1,400 units	1,260 units	1,000 units

30% of credit customers pay the month after the sale, with the remaining 70% received two months after the sale.

Complete the receipts schedule below to identify the total sales values for each month, the split between cash and credit sales, and the timing of cash inflows from credit sales.

	Total sales £	Cash sales £	Credit sales £	30% £	Month credit sales received	70% £	Month credit sales received
September							
October							
November							

Task 1.5

The usual cash payment timings for an organisation are as follows:

Type of payment	Timing of payment
Purchases of materials	40% one month after purchase, 60% two months after purchase
Wages and salaries	Month incurred
Other production expenses	One month after incurred
Administrative expenses	Two months after incurred

The organisation has also forecast the following costs for the period January to June:

Month	Purchases of materials £	Wages and salaries £	Other production expenses £	Administrative expenses £
January	35,000	12,200	11,450	6,550
February	38,500	13,100	12,300	7,080
March	37,000	12,800	10,980	6,970
April	39,600	13,250	11,580	6,600
May	38,200	13,900	12,690	7,150
June	39,100	14,000	11,400	8,000

Other production expenses include a monthly machinery depreciation charge of £780.

Complete the following extract from the payments section of the cash budget for the organisation for the months of April, May and June.

Cash Budget Payments (extract)	April £	May £	June £
Purchase of materials - February	23,100		
Purchase of materials - March	14,800	22,200	
Purchase of materials - April		15,840	23,760
Purchase of materials - May			15,280
Wages and salaries	13,250	13,900	14,000
Other production expenses	10,200	10,800	11,910
Administrative expenses	7,080	6,970	6,600
Total payments	68,430	69,710	71,550

Task 1.6

The cash budget for Boileroom Industries Limited for the three months ended June has been partially completed. The following information is to be incorporated and the cash budget completed.

- An invitation to current shareholders to purchase additional shares is being prepared. This is expected to generate £125,000 cash during May. Legal costs of £11,000 in connection with the share issue need to be paid in April.

- The business is planning to purchase and install new production equipment and use a training company to train the staff in its use. Purchase costs of £100,000 will be incurred in April, and installation costs of £15,000 will need to be paid in May. The training cost of £12,000 will also need to be paid in May.

- When Boileroom Industries Limited uses its bank overdraft facility interest is payable monthly and is estimated at 1.5% of the previous month's overdraft balance. The interest is to be rounded to the nearest £.

- At 1 April the balance of the bank account was overdrawn £10,500.

Using the additional information above, complete the cash budget for Boileroom Industries Limited for the three months ending June. Cash inflows should be entered as positive figures and cash outflows as negative figures. Zero must be entered where appropriate.

	April £	May £	June £
RECEIPTS			
Cash sales	20,950	21,010	19,990
Credit sales	154,320	133,500	141,650
Share issue			
Total receipts			
PAYMENTS			
Purchases	-88,560	-93,480	-90,560
Wages	-52,450	-53,480	-52,570
Expenses	-31,050	-30,990	-32,690
Purchase & installation of Production equipment			
Training costs			
Legal costs re share issue			
Overdraft interest			
Total payments			
Net cash flow			
Opening bank balance			
Closing bank balance			

SECTION 2

Task 2.1

A company has prepared a cash budget for the first five periods of trading of a new branch that is to be opened. Each period is 30 days.

Each product has a budgeted selling price of £50, and all sales are made on credit.

The original budget estimates have now been revised.

	Period 1	Period 2	Period 3	Period 4	Period 5
Original budgeted sales volume (units)	2,350	2,560	2,660	2,800	3,000
Revised budgeted sales volume (units)	2,180	2,400	2,510	2,720	2,860

The sales receipts pattern has been estimated as follows:

	30 days after sale	60 days after sale	90 days after sale
Original pattern	70%	30%	
Revised pattern	60%	20%	20%

The original receipts pattern assumed no irrecoverable debts, but the revised percentages are after deducting an allowance of 4% of sales for irrecoverable debts.

(a) Complete the table below to show the revised sales values and revised timing of sales receipts.

	Period 1 £	Period 2 £	Period 3 £	Period 4 £
Original sales value	117,500	128,000	133,000	
Revised sales value				
Original timing of receipts		82,250	124,850	131,500
Revised timing of receipts				

Additional information

The material cost for each product was budgeted at £20 per unit, with payment being made in the month following purchase.

The company has now negotiated a 10% discount provided payment is made in the month of purchase.

The company does not intend to maintain any inventory of materials or finished goods, and will therefore purchase materials in the month of sale.

(b) Complete the table below to show the revised forecast amounts and timing of payments for purchases in periods 1 to 4. Assume that the discount is taken. Use minus signs to denote cash outflows.

	Period 1 £	Period 2 £	Period 3 £	Period 4 £
Payment for purchases				

(c) Calculate the budgeted cash balance at the end of period 4, assuming that the branch commences period 1 with a cash receipt of £15,000 from the company head office. Assume that there were payments totalling £85,000 for labour and expenses in addition to the payments for materials. Use minus signs to denote outflows.

	Amount £
Receipt from head office	
Total receipts from sales	
Total payments for purchases	
Total payments for labour and expenses	
Closing cash balance	

Task 2.2

(a) An organisation has encountered various issues. Select from the options provided the most appropriate action to deal with each issue. The action selected should ensure that cash inflows are maximised and cash outflows are minimised without adversely affecting sales or production.

Issue	Action
1. A major competitor has increased its selling prices by 2%	
2. There is insufficient work for the production staff leading to increased idle time	
3. Interest on a £50,000 loan is being paid at base rate plus 8%. The base rate is expected to rise	
4. Prompt payment discount of 1% for payment in 7 days is offered to customers, but very few take the discount	
5. A major supplier is offering to freeze prices in return for a long term contract	

Select actions from the following:

(a) Change suppliers

(b) Offer more favourable prompt payment discounts

(c) Pay off the loan by using an overdraft

(d) Stop offering prompt payment discounts

(e) Increase overtime working

(f) Increase supervision of production staff

(g) Increase selling prices in line with competitors

(h) Negotiate a fixed rate loan

(i) Consider signing long term contract with supplier

(j) Manage a reduction in production staff through natural wastage

(k) Reduce selling prices

(l) Reduce supervision of production staff

(b) The quarterly budgeted and actual figures for an organisation are provided below:

	Budgeted £	Actual £
Receipts from credit customers	251,300	225,950
Cash sales	45,300	53,250
Payments to credit suppliers	(149,500)	(151,400)
Cash purchases	(12,320)	(10,400)
Capital expenditure	(32,950)	(34,000)
Wages and salaries	(41,230)	(40,980)
General expenses	(51,020)	(58,990)
Net cash flow	9,580	(16,570)
Opening bank balance	(22,480)	(22,480)
Closing bank balance	(12,900)	(39,050)

Prepare a reconciliation of budgeted cash flow with actual cash flow for the quarter. Select the appropriate description for each entry, and show + or − signs to denote increased or reduced cash. Ensure that the reconciliation balances.

	£
Budgeted closing bank balance	
Surplus/Shortfall in receipts from credit customers	
Surplus/Shortfall in cash sales	
Increase/Decrease in payments to credit suppliers	
Increase/Decrease in cash purchases	
Increase/Decrease in capital expenditure	
Increase/Decrease in wages and salaries	
Increase/Decrease in general expenses	
Actual closing bank balance	

(c) Select from the following list the **one** action that would have had the greatest impact on bringing the actual closing bank balance closer to the budgeted balance.

	✔
Ensure that capital expenditure was in line with budget	
Reduce overtime working in line with budget	
Improve credit control so that customers pay in line with budget	
Encourage more cash customers to pay on credit	

Task 2.3

(a) Indicate with a tick the product features which relate to a bank business overdraft.

	✔
Interest is calculated on the amount that is actually borrowed	
It is suitable for long-term financing	
The customer can borrow an unlimited amount at any time	
Security is normally required	

(b) Indicate with a tick the product features which relate to a bank business loan.

	✔
It is normally used for long-term finance	
A facility letter is not normally required	
Interest is normally lower than overdraft interest	
It is only available at a capped rate of interest	

Task 2.4

Mistery Limited is a small company which manufactures giftware products.

A cash budget has recently been drawn up projecting the month-end bank balances for the year.

Overdrawn balances are shown in brackets.

month	£
January	5,500
February	(2,400)
March	(6,400)
April	3,275
May	4,961
June	(1,200)
July	(8,800)
August	(7,200)
September	560
October	8,905
November	(1,800)
December	3,472

The directors of Mistery Ltd realise that the cash shortfall during the year will have to be financed by the bank. They meet with the bank business manager who offers two options:

Option 1

A bank overdraft. The cost of this will be:

- Arrangement fee of £350

- Interest charged at 12% per annum (ie 1% a month). Interest is charged monthly on the end-of-month overdrawn bank balances.

Option 2

A short-term bank loan for the year of £9,000. The cost of this (including interest) will be:

- Arrangement fee of £150

- 12 monthly repayments of £825.

You have been asked by Fred Dymock, the Finance Director, to assess these two propositions in terms of the cost of the finance. You have drafted the email which follows on the next page. You are to:

(a) Calculate the interest cost for the year of the two options. Enter them in the appropriate grey boxes in the text of the email.

(b) Fill in the white boxes in the email using items from the following list:

£150 £8,800 £1,050 £628 £350

overdraft   **less flexible**   **options for raising finance**   **short-term loan**   **more flexible**

EMAIL

To: fd@mistery.co.uk
From: astudent@mistery.co.uk
Date: today
Subject: [   ]

As requested, I set out an analysis of the cost of the two options for raising finance from the bank.

The maximum amount owing during the year is [   ] (in July), and this will need to be covered by the finance.

The overdraft option will cost a maximum of [   ], which is made up of the arrangement fee of [   ] and total interest during the year of [   ].

The short-term bank loan option will cost a maximum of [   ], which includes the arrangement fee of [   ] and total interest during the year of [   ].

I recommend the [   ] as it is [   ] and costs less than the other option.

Task 2.5

(a)   Your company treasurer asks about the risk factor of four different investments and also whether they are normally held for the short term or long term. Tick the appropriate boxes in the table below.

Type of investment	higher risk ✔	lower risk ✔	short-term ✔	long-term ✔
Money market deposits				
UK Government stock				
Stocks and shares				
Certificates of deposit				

(b)   There are a number of functions of a company Treasury Department. Indicate with a tick in the table below whether each of the following is true or false.

Function of a Treasury Department	True ✔	False ✔
Investment of surplus funds		
Control of the company's sales ledger		
Planning the raising of finance		
Assessing the risk of the company's investments		
Recruiting new staff		

Task 2.6

(a) Your company treasury regularly invests in a range of short-term investments.

You are to state whether the following investment suggestions are likely to give a higher or a lower interest rate paid on the investments:

Investment	higher ✔	lower ✔
Bank 'instant' deposit account - no notice of withdrawal required and no minimum amount to be deposited		
Bank 'notice' deposit account - 30 days notice of withdrawal required and no minimum amount to be deposited		
Bank 'treasury' deposit account - no notice of withdrawal and a minimum investment of £250,000 to be deposited		
Bank deposit account - no notice of withdrawal required and no minimum amount to be deposited, but the bank is known to carry a high level of risk		

(b) Your company has a standard policy for the investment of surplus short-term funds. The rules are:

- The investment must be convertible into cash within one month.

- The maximum amount to be invested in any one type of investment is £250,000.

- The interest rate of the investment must be at least 1% over bank base rate.

- The risk factor of the investment must be low and the funds must not be invested in any form of stocks and shares or funds investing in shares, commodities or property.

Your company has just sold some property and the sale proceeds of £200,000 need to be invested for the short-term because the money will soon be required for the purchase of new equipment. Bank base rate is 2%.

The following three investment options are suggested:

Option 1
A bank six month deposit offering 2% over base rate. Minimum investment £500,000.

Option 2
A bank no notice deposit offering 1.5% over base rate. Minimum investment £250,000.

Option 3
A bank one year 'stock market performance bond' offering a rate of return equivalent to 4% over base rate. Minimum investment £500,000.

You are to complete the table below for all three investment options by ticking the boxes which indicate that the investment policy guidelines will be followed.

Policy requirement for short-term investments	Option 1 ✔	Option 2 ✔	Option 3 ✔
Convertible to cash within one month			
Maximum investment of £250,000			
Interest rate at least 1% over bank base rate			
Low risk factor and no investment related to returns on stocks and shares			

(c)   Indicate in the table below which (if any) of the above three options you would recommend as a result of your analysis.

	✔
Option 1	
Option 2	
Option 3	
None of the options	

Cash management
Practice assessment 1 answers

SECTION 1

Task 1.1

(a)

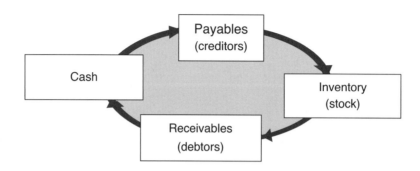

(b)   The cash operating cycle in days for the business is

121 days

(c)   Over-capitalisation can occur when a business has **too much** working capital and over-trading can occur when a business has **insufficient** working capital.

Signs of over-capitalisation include **high** inventory levels, **high** cash levels, **high** receivables (debtors) levels, and suppliers being paid **early**.

Task 1.2

(a)

Example	Capital payment	Regular revenue payment	Payment for drawings	Exceptional payment
Purchase of machinery	✓			
Loan repayments		✓		
Purchase of shares to take over another company				✓
Final dividends			✓	
Salary payments		✓		
Bank interest payments		✓		

Task 1.2 (b)

	£	*Workings (in £)*
Sales receipts	103,740	103,900 + 680 - 840
Purchases payments	45,610	45,090 + 8,450 – 7,930
Wages paid	26,430	No adjustment
Rent paid	8,500	9,000 – 1,500 + 1,000
Shop expenses	5,860	5,950 + 120 - 210
Depreciation	0	Non cash item
Bank interest	245	190 + 55
Drawings	15,000	Per narrative

Task 1.3

(a)

	Sales volume (units)	Trend	Monthly variation (volume less trend)
August	40,900		
September	47,300	42,300	+5,000
October	38,700	42,600	-3,900
November	41,800	42,900	-1,100
December	48,200		

The monthly sales volume trend is 300 units.

(b)

	Forecast trend	Variation	Forecast sales volume	Forecast sales £	Forecast purchases £
January	43,500	-3,900	39,600	316,800	174,240

(c)   £24,058

Task 1.4

(a)

	Actual		Forecast			
	January	**February**	**March**	**April**	**May**	**June**
Total sales	48,100	49,600	49,000	52,500	51,600	49,400
Cash sales	12,025	12,400	12,250	13,125	12,900	12,350
Credit sales	36,075	37,200	36,750	39,375	38,700	37,050

(b)

	CASH RECEIVED					
	Credit sales	**February**	**March**	**April**	**May**	**June**
	£	£	£	£	£	£
January	36,075	14,430	21,645			
February	37,200		14,880	22,320		
March	36,750			14,700	22,050	
April	39,375				15,750	23,625
May	38,700					15,480
Monthly credit sales receipts			36,525	37,020	37,800	39,105

Task 1.5

	October	November	December
	£	£	£
Purchases	49,996	52,548	55,100
Wages	12,800	12,960	14,500
Expenses	9,050	7,450	10,100
New machine	13,375	13,375	13,375
Total payments	85,221	86,333	93,075

Task 1.6

	April	May	June
	£	£	£
RECEIPTS			
Cash sales	18,800	19,180	20,480
Credit sales	43,085	43,520	54,852
Bank loan	75,000	0	0
Total receipts	136,885	62,700	75,332
PAYMENTS			
Purchases	-46,650	-47,005	-42,075
Wages	-18,800	-18,950	-18,450
Expenses	-10,350	-11,260	-13,260
Capital expenditure	0	-79,500	0
Bank loan capital repayment	0	-1,250	-1,250
Bank loan interest	0	-500	-500
Overdraft interest	-27	0	-721
Total payments	-75,827	-158,465	76,256
Net cash flow	61,058	-95,765	-924
Opening bank balance	-1,350	59,708	-36,057
Closing bank balance	59,708	-36,057	-36,981

SECTION 2

Task 2.1

(a)

	Period 1 *(£)*	Period 2 *(£)*	Period 3 *(£)*	Period 4 *(£)*	Period 5 *(£)*
Original value of forecast sales	35,600	39,200	38,000	34,000	38,400
Original timing of receipts			38,600	36,000	36,200
Revised value of forecast sales	33,820	37,240	36,100	32,300	36,480
Revised timing of receipts			36,328	35,568	33,896

SECTION 2

Task 2.1

(b)

	Period 3 *(£)*	Period 4 *(£)*	Period 5 *(£)*
Original timing of payments	21,200	20,800	22,600
Revised timing of payments	21,080	21,340	22,720

(c)

	Period 3 *(£)*	Period 4 *(£)*	Period 5 *(£)*
Changes in sales receipts	-2,272	-432	-2,304
Changes in purchase payments	+120	-540	-120
Net change	-2,152	-972	-2,424

Task 2.2   (a)

	£
Budgeted closing bank balance	18,910
Shortfall in receipts from credit customers	-4,860
Surplus in cash sales	+4,980
Increase in payments to credit suppliers	-740
Decrease in cash purchases	+1,510
Increase in capital expenditure	-23,500
Increase in wages and salaries	-850
Increase in general expenses	-564
Actual closing bank balance	-5,114

(b)   Made any payments for capital expenditure in line with the budget

(c)   Labour costs have increased   ➡   Reduce use of agency staff

Sales volumes have decreased   ➡   Improve marketing

Inventory levels have increased   ➡   Improve stock control

Customers are taking more days to settle their debts   ➡   Improve credit control

Prices of raw materials have increased   ➡   Negotiate improved prices

Task 2.3

(a) It is useful for covering working capital requirements

The account will normally fluctuate from debit (borrowing) to credit (money in the account)

(b) Often used for non-current (fixed) asset purchases

Can be repaid in full at the end of the loan period

(c) A facility letter is a document drawn up by the **bank** and signed by the **customer** in respect of the granting of bank finance. it sets out the **amount** of the finance and the **security** requirements. Common clauses include a **default** clause to provide the bank with legal rights and remedies if the customer fails to repay the borrowing.

Task 2.4

(a)

	loan interest	arrangement fees	overdraft interest	total cost
	£	£	£	£
Option 1	6,000	1,625	1,050	8,675
Option 2	7,500	2,500	–	10,000

(b) Option 1

(c) Option 2

(d) The amount due in interest payments will be higher

The amount due in capital repayment of the loan will be lower

Task 2.5 The **Gilts** market provides long term funding for the UK Government. This is a relatively **low risk** investment. Another way of providing funding for the UK Government is investing in the **Treasury Bill** market. This is a **short-term**. form of investment. Investment in company shares on the Stock Market can be relatively **high-risk** and should only be seen as a long-term investment.

Task 2.6

(a)

	Convertible within 60 days *(yes/no)*	Available for £200,000 *(yes/no)*	Interest rate 1% over base *(yes/no)*	Overseas investment *(yes/no)*	Level of risk acceptable *(yes/no)*
Option 1	yes	yes	yes	no	no
Option 2	yes	yes	yes	yes	yes
Option 3	no	no	yes	yes	yes
Option 4	no	yes	yes	no	yes

(b)   Option 2 – Mercia Bank plc money market account

Cash management

Practice assessment 2 answers

SECTION 1

Task 1.1

(a)

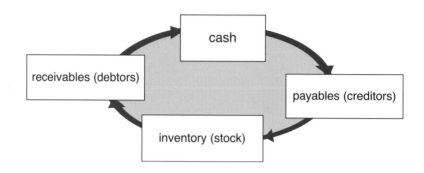

(b)   94 + 58 – 75 = 77 so correct choice is C

Note: incorrect answers calculated as:

94 – 58 + 75 = 111

58 + 75 – 94 = 39

94 + 58 + 75 = 227

(c)   Over-trading can occur when a business has **insufficient** working capital and over-capitalisation can occur when a business has **too much** working capital.

Signs of over-trading include **rapidly increasing** sales volumes, **reducing** profit margins, **longer** receivable (debtor) collection periods, **longer** payable (creditor) payment periods.

Task 1.2

(a)

Type of receipt or payment	Description
Capital payments	Payments that relate to the acquisition of non-current assets (fixed assets)
Regular revenue receipts	Income received from the operating activities of the business that are expected to occur frequently
Drawings	Payments made to the owners of the business
Exceptional payments	Payments that do not arise from the operating activities of the business and that are not expected to occur frequently

Task 1.2 (b)

	£	*Workings*
Sales receipts	187,620	182,400 + 21,620 – 16,400
Purchases payments	26,996	27,360 + 760 – 1,124
Wages paid	72,900	No adjustment
Rent paid	12,900	12,650 – 1,200 +1,450
Office expenses	18,518	18,640 + 119 – 241
Van expenses	24,202	24,118 – 483 + 567
Van depreciation	0	Non- cash item

Task 1.3

(a)

	Sales volume (units)	**Trend**	**Monthly variation** (volume less trend)
August	9,360		
September	5,940	6,840	-900
October	5,220	7,020	–1,800
November	9,900	7,200	+ 2,700
December	6,480		

The monthly sales volume trend is 180 units.

(b)

	Forecast trend	Variation	Forecast sales volume	Forecast sales £	Forecast purchases £
January	7,560	-1,800	5,760	46,080	18,432

(c)   £6,220 ÷ 163 x 193 = **7,365**

Note:

incorrect answers calculated as:

£6,220 ÷ 193 x 163 = 5,253

£6,220 ÷ 186 x 193 = 6,454

£6,220 ÷ 193 x 186 = 5,994

Task 1.4

(a)

	Actual		Forecast			
	January	**February**	**March**	**April**	**May**	**June**
Total sales	37,500	42,000	45,000	51,000	58,000	63,750
Cash sales (12%)	4,500	5,040	5,400	6,120	6,960	7,650
Credit sales (88%)	33,000	36,960	39,600	44,880	51,040	56,100

(b)

	CASH RECEIVED					
	Credit sales	**February**	**March**	**April**	**May**	**June**
	£	£	£	£	£	£
January	33,000	19,800	13,200			
February	36,960		22,176	14,784		
March	39,600			23,760	15,840	
April	44,880				26,928	17,952
May	51,040					30,624
Monthly credit sales receipts			35,376	38,544	42,768	48,576

Task 1.5

	October	November	December
	£	£	£
Payments			
Purchases	46,915	48,950	49,830
Wages	12,300	12,300	12,750
Expenses	7,470	8,836	7,652
New machine	15,000	15,000	15,000
Total payments	81,685	85,086	85,232

Task 1.6

	April	May	June
	£	£	£
RECEIPTS			
Cash sales	8,100	9,180	10,440
Credit sales	53,064	53,516	64,152
Bank loan	43200	0	0
Total receipts	104,364	62,696	74,592
Payments			
Purchases	-34,650	-37,125	-42,075
Wages	-18,000	-18,450	-18,450
Expenses	-10,318	-11,269	-13,254
Capital expenditure	0	-49,500	0
Bank loan capital repayment	0	-900	-900
Bank loan interest	0	-180	-180
Overdraft interest	0	0	-91
Total payments	-62,968	-117,424	-74,950
Net cash flow	41,396	-54,728	-358
Opening bank balance	4,232	45,628	-9,100
Closing bank balance	45,628	-9,100	-9,458

SECTION 2

Task 2.1

(a)

	Period 1 *(£)*	Period 2 *(£)*	Period 3 *(£)*	Period 4 *(£)*	Period 5 *(£)*
Original value of forecast sales	27,600	28,800	29,520	30,240	31,200
Original timing of receipts			29,160	29,880	30,720
Revised value of forecast sales	23,460	24,480	25,092	25,704	26,520
Revised timing of receipts			24,378	25,092	25,755

Task 2.1

(b)

	Period 3 *(£)*	Period 4 *(£)*	Period 5 *(£)*
Original timing of payments	9,600	9,820	10,940
Revised timing of payments	8,816	9,666	10,156

(c)

	Period 3 *(£)*	Period 4 *(£)*	Period 5 *(£)*
Changes in sales receipts	-4,782	-4,788	-4,965
Changes in purchase payments	784	154	784
Net change	-3,998	-4,634	-4,181

Task 2.2 (a)

	£
Budgeted closing bank balance	10,905
Shortfall in receipts from receivables (debtors)	(4,756)
Shortfall in cash sales	(2,570)
Increase in payments to payables (creditors)	(2,173)
Increase in cash purchases	(340)
Increase in capital expenditure	(28,000)
Decrease in wages and salaries	1,600
Decrease in general expenses	2,186
Actual closing bank balance	(23,148)

(b) (c) Delayed capital expenditure

(Note: Although the other options could have resulted in a lower overdraft they are not sufficient in and of themselves to reduce the deficit by £23,148)

(c)

Labour costs have increased	➤	Reduce overtime working
Sales volumes have decreased	➤	Improve the product
Payments to suppliers are being made earlier	➤	Negotiate early settlement discount
Customers are taking more days to settle their debts	➤	Improve credit control
Prices of raw materials have increased	➤	Change suppliers

Task 2.3

(a)   Interest rates are high; it is repayable on demand; it is a short-term form of finance.

(b)   Interest rates are low; repayments can be negotiated; it is useful for capital purchases.

(c)   A bank facility letter sets out the **legal** rights and duties of **the bank and the customer** when the bank grants **overdrafts and loans**.

The purpose of a facility letter is to protect the rights of **the bank and the customer**.

Task 2.4

(a)

	Loan interest £	Arrangement fee £	Overdraft interest £	Total cost £
Option 1	4,680	780	1,280	6,740
Option 2	6,240	720	0	6,960
Option 3	3,840	0	0	3,840

(b)   Option 1

Task 2.5

Certificates of deposit are certificates issued by **banks** that certify that an amount of money has been deposited and will be repaid at a specific date in the future. They **can** be traded on a market. They are considered to be a **low risk** investment.

Local authority short-term loans are certificates issued by **local authorities** and backed by the government. They **can** be traded on a market. They are considered to be a **low risk investment.**

Government securities are also known as **gilt-edged** securities and **can** be traded. Interest rates are **fixed** and these types of securities are considered to be **low risk** because **they are** backed by the government.

Task 2.6

(a)

	Convertible within 60 days	Investment £50,000 or below	Interest rate 2% above base	Investment does not include shares	Risk
Option 1	no	yes	yes	no	yes
Option 2	yes	yes	no	yes	yes
Option 3	yes	yes	yes	no	no
Option 4	yes	no	yes	yes	yes

(b)   The company should select **none of the options**.

Cash management

Practice assessment 3 answers

SECTION 1

Task 1.1

(a)   (a) and (d) are TRUE; (b) and (c) are FALSE.

(b)   (d) reduce by 23 days

(c)   (a) is INCORRECT; the remainder are CORRECT

Task 1.2

(a)   (a) and (d) are FALSE; (b) and (c) are TRUE

(b)   £56,600

(c)   £325,165

(d)   (b)   Payments to acquire non-current assets

Task 1.3

(a)

	Sales value £	Trend £
August	163,600	
September	189,200	169,200
October	154,800	170,400
November	167,200	171,600
December	192,800	

The monthly sales value trend is £**1,200**

(b)   The monthly sales volume trend is **48** units

(c)

	Trend £	Monthly Variation £	Forecast Sales Value £
January	174,000	-15,600	158,400
February	175,200	-4,400	170,800
March	176,400	+20,000	196,400

(d)   In future, the direct labour cost to manufacture 20,000 units will be **£48,925**

Task 1.4

	Total sales £	Cash sales £	Credit sales £	30%	Month credit sales received	70%	Month credit sales received
September	66,000	16,500	49,500	14,850	Oct	34,650	Nov
October	84,000	21,000	63,000	18,900	Nov	44,100	Dec
November	75,600	18,900	56,700	17,010	Dec	39,690	Jan

Task 1.5

Cash Budget Payments (extract)	April £	May £	June £
Purchase of materials - February	23,100		
Purchase of materials - March	14,800	22,200	
Purchase of materials - April		15,840	23,760
Purchase of materials - May			15,280
Wages and salaries	13,250	13,900	14,000
Other production expenses	10,200	10,800	11,910
Administrative expenses	7,080	6,970	6,600
Total payments	68,430	69,710	71,550

Task 1.6

	April £	May £	June £
RECEIPTS			
Cash sales	20,950	21,010	19,990
Credit sales	154,320	133,500	141,650
Share issue	0	125,000	0
Total receipts	175,270	279,510	161,640
PAYMENTS			
Purchases	-88,560	-93,480	-90,560
Wages	-52,450	-53,480	-52,570
Expenses	-31,050	-30,990	-32,690
Purchase & installation of Production equipment	-100,000	-15,000	-0
Training costs	-0	-12,000	-0
Legal costs re share issue	-11,000	-0	-0
Overdraft interest	-158	-1,777	-685
Total payments	-283,218	-206,727	-176,505
Net cash flow	-107,948	72,783	-14,865
Opening bank balance	-10,500	-118,448	-45,665
Closing bank balance	-118,448	-45,665	-60,530

SECTION 2

Task 2.1

(a)

	Period 1 £	Period 2 £	Period 3 £	Period 4 £
Original sales value	117,500	128,000	133,000	
Revised sales value	109,000	120,000	125,500	
Original timing of receipts		82,250	124,850	131,500
Revised timing of receipts		62,784	90,048	116,256

(b)

	Period 1 £	Period 2 £	Period 3 £	Period 4 £
Payment for purchases	39,240	43,200	45,180	48,960

(c)

	Amount £
Receipt from head office	15,000
Total receipts from sales	269,088
Total payments for purchases	-176,580
Total payments for labour and expenses	-85,000
Closing cash balance	22,508

Task 2.2

(a)

Issue		Action
1.	A major competitor has increased its selling prices by 2%	(g)
2.	There is insufficient work for the production staff leading to increased idle time	(j)
3.	Interest on a £50,000 loan is being paid at base rate plus 8%. The base rate is expected to rise.	(h)
4.	Prompt payment discount of 1% for payment in 7 days is offered to customers, but very few take the discount	(b)
5.	A major supplier is offering to freeze prices in return for a long term contract	(i)

(b)   Offer more favourable prompt payment discounts

(g)   Increase selling price in line with competitors

(h)   Negotiate a fixed rate loan

(i)   Consider signing long term contract with supplier

(j)   Manage a reduction in production staff through natural wastage

(b)

	£
Budgeted closing bank balance	-12,900
Shortfall in receipts from credit customers	-25,350
Surplus in cash sales	7,950
Increase in payments to credit suppliers	-1,900
Decrease in cash purchases	1,920
Increase in capital expenditure	-1,050
Decrease in wages and salaries	250
Increase in general expenses	-7,970
Actual closing bank balance	-39,050

(c)   Improve credit control so that customers pay in line with budget

Task 2.3

(a)

Interest is calculated on the amount that is actually borrowed	✔
It is suitable for long-term financing	
The customer can borrow an unlimited amount at any time	
Security is normally required	✔

(b)

It is normally used for long-term finance	✔
A facility letter is not normally required	
Interest is normally lower than overdraft interest	✔
It is only available at a capped rate of interest	

Task 2.4 (a) and (b)

EMAIL

To: fd@mistery.co.uk
From: astudent@mistery.co.uk
Date: today
Subject: **options for raising finance**

As requested, I set out an analysis of the cost of the two options for raising finance from the bank.

The maximum amount owing during the year is **£8,800** (in July), and this will need to be covered by the finance.

The overdraft option will cost a maximum of **£628,** which is made up of the arrangement fee of **£350** and total interest during the year of **£278** *(24 + 64 + 12 + 88 + 72 + 18)*

The short-term bank loan option will cost a maximum of **£1,050,** which includes the arrangement fee of **£150** and total interest during the year of **£900.**

I recommend the **overdraft** as it is **more flexible** and costs less than the other option.

Task 2.5

(a)

Type of investment	higher risk ✔	lower risk ✔	short-term ✔	long-term ✔
Money market deposits		✔	✔	
UK Government stock		✔		✔
Stocks and shares	✔			✔
Certificates of deposit		✔	✔	

(b)

Function of a Treasury Department	True ✔	False ✔
Investment of surplus funds	✔	
Control of the company's sales ledger		✔
Planning the raising of finance	✔	
Assessing the risk of the company's investments	✔	
Recruiting new staff		✔

Task 2.6

(a)

Investment	higher ✔	lower ✔
Bank 'instant' deposit account - no notice of withdrawal required and no minimum amount to be deposited		✔
Bank 'notice' deposit account - 30 days notice of withdrawal required and no minimum amount to be deposited	✔	
Bank 'treasury' deposit account - no notice of withdrawal and a minimum investment of £250,000 to be deposited	✔	
Bank deposit account - no notice of withdrawal required and no minimum amount to be deposited, but the bank is known to carry a high level of risk	✔	

(b)

Policy requirement for short-term investments	Option 1 ✔	Option 2 ✔	Option 3 ✔
Convertible to cash within one month		✔	
Maximum investment of £250,000		✔	✔
Interest rate at least 1% over bank base rate	✔	✔	✔
Low risk factor and no investment related to returns on stocks and shares	✔	✔	

(c)   Option 2

for your notes

for your notes

for your notes